METEORITES

METEORITES

FRITZ HEIDE

Translated by EDWARD ANDERS in collaboration
with EUGENE R. DuFRESNE

THE UNIVERSITY OF CHICAGO PRESS
Chicago and London

This book is a translation of
Kleine Meteoritenkunde, second edition 1957,
published by Springer Verlag, Berlin

SBN: 226-00000-0 (cloth bound); 226-00000-0 (paper bound)
Library of Congress Catalog Card Number: 63–20906

THE UNIVERSITY OF CHICAGO PRESS, CHICAGO 60637
The University of Chicago Press, Ltd., London

TRANSLATOR'S PREFACE

When the late F. Paneth reviewed the 1957 edition of Heide's *Kleine Meteoritenkunde* he said: "As long as no bigger *Meteoritenkunde* [in the sense of Cohen's six-volume treatise] is available, this little volume . . . is the best guide to the subject for the serious student as well as for the amateur." He went on to say that while one might be tempted to recommend an English translation of this book, he was not in favor of it, because "it can be assumed that most scientifically minded people, especially students at universities, know at least a little German."

In spite of Professor Paneth's reservations, I decided to translate the book. Research on meteorites has accelerated a great deal in the last fifteen years, particularly since the advent of the space age; yet formal instruction in this field is virtually non-existent. Even the experts are largely self-taught. Repeatedly, I have been asked by laymen, students, and prospective researchers to recommend a good introductory book on the subject. When I saw how their quickly aroused enthusiasm was dampened once I mentioned that Heide's book was written in German, I had no choice but to translate it. In this task, I was fortunate in securing the assistance of Dr. E. R. DuFresne, who did most of the preliminary editing of the rough translation.

The present version, while based on the 1957 German edition, has been revised and updated in many places. Professor Heide himself supplied most of these revisions; others were contributed by the translators, either as changes in the text, or as "translator's notes." The latter were used whenever we were not sure of Professor Heide's concurrence with our views. Revisions were particularly extensive in the section on meteorite ages, where several pages were completely rewritten. Of the tables, Nos. 8, 11, 13, 14, 20, 21, and 22 and the appendix tables were revised or replaced, to take into account the latest data. Two new figures (Figs. 96 and 97) were added, and six other figures were replaced by more recent versions, some taken from Brian Mason's excellent book *Meteorites* (Wiley, 1962). A list of German meteorites was deleted from the Appendix. I did not think it advisable to replace it by a list of United States meteorites, since such a list has already appeared in Mason's book.

I also decided to retain the metric system in the text, on the grounds that any person sophisticated enough to worry about meteorites should have no trouble in visualizing distances and weights in metric units. The following conversion table may be useful:

1 meter (m.) = 100 centimeters (cm.) = 1/1,000 kilometers (km.) = 39.3 inches.
1 kilogram (kg.) = 1,000 grams = 1/1,000 (metric) ton = 2.20 lbs. = 35.2 ounces.

For the benefit of those readers who wish to pursue the subject further, I am including a few references. Brian Mason's book *Meteorites* (see above) is probably the best all-round work on the subject. Fletcher G. Watson's *Between the Planets* (Anchor Books, 1962) treats meteorites largely from the astronomer's point of view and contains a good deal of material on meteors, comets, and asteroids. Two chapters in Volume IV of *The Solar System,* edited by G. P. Kuiper and B. M. Middlehurst (University of Chicago Press, 1963) deal with the chemistry and physics, and with the ages of meteorites. (An earlier version of the latter also appeared in *Rev. Mod. Phys.* 34, 287 [1962]). The origin of meteorites has been reviewed by G. G. Goles and myself (*J. Chem. Ed.* 38, 58 [1961]), but many other points of view exist and must not be overlooked (H. C. Urey, *J. Geophys. Res.* 64, 1721 [1959], J. A. Wood, *Icarus,* to be published 1963). The petrology of meteorites was covered in 1885 in G. Tschermak's classic work on the microscopic constitution of meteorites, now available in an English translation by J. A. Wood (Smithsonian Institution, 1963). The metallurgy of iron meteorites was described by S. H. Perry in the monograph "The metallography of meteoritic iron" (Bull. U.S. Nat. Museum, 184, 1944), and the data have been interpreted by many authors (see Mason's book for references).

It is a pleasure to acknowledge the able assistance of Miss Kay Miller and Mrs. Florence Ripkey, who transcribed a tape recording of the translation, undaunted by the phonetic complexities of meteorite names.

EDWARD ANDERS

CONTENTS

INTRODUCTION

All readers of this book must have seen a shooting star: a mere dot of light that dashes among the fixed stars and silently disappears. Many will also have seen a meteor, a large fireball, with a striking flare that radiates bluish-white or reddish-yellow light and that hurries quietly across the sky and disappears behind the horizon or suddenly winks out. Only a few people are likely to have seen a meteorite fall: a large fireball with a long, glowing train crosses the sky, and night becomes as bright as day. Hissing, clattering, and thundering noises are heard, followed by an explosion-like report. The whole train of events, which lasts only a few seconds, can easily be observed even should it occur in broad daylight. Solid bodies fall from the sky, and fragments of a stony or metallic nature are found in the pits formed on impact.

Each of these three types of celestial phenomenon is the result of a collision between the earth and a solid body from outer space. But only meteorites succeed in penetrating the atmosphere to hit the surface of the earth. This is what makes the meteorites so important to us. We are conscious of the moon, the sun, and the stars only through the visible or invisible rays which they emit. This also applies to meteors and shooting stars. True, we have ingenious instruments to analyze these rays, giving us rather accurate knowledge of the material composition of these celestial bodies. But many questions cannot be answered by these methods. Meteorites, on the other hand, can be analyzed using the mineralogical, chemical, and physical methods that we also apply to materials from the solid crust of our earth. Hence, we are able to give satisfactory answers to quite a few of the questions raised by the existence of these missiles from the sky.

These questions are of more than purely academic interest. Knowledge of the composition of meteorites permits us to draw important conclusions about the structure and composition of our own planet and to recognize certain laws that are of great importance in the study of the distribution of matter on the earth. Since these laws also govern such things as the formation of ore deposits of useful minerals, their importance for the cultural and economic life of mankind needs no emphasis.

Meteorites can also affect human life more directly. Cosmic missiles, which bombard the earth as it travels through space, have so far caused scarcely any damage. But there is evidence that meteorites occasionally reach gigantic size and that their impact on the earth is accompanied by huge explosions.

In this book we are concerned with the questions that might be raised by a man holding a meteorite in his hand. Shooting stars and meteors that burn up at quite high altitudes, sending no more than their light to earth, will be included only insofar as they have some relation to the meteorites.

The name meteorite is derived from the Greek. It means approximately "present in the air." In old books and ancient chronicles one frequently finds other names, usually based on some assumption of their origin or on some phenomenon of the accompanying fall. For example, aerolites, or air stones; siderolites, or sky stones, not to mention "moon stones" and "thunder stones." Meteorites have even been called baethylia, or animated stones.

I. FALL PHENOMENA

LIGHT

The first signs by which the approach of a meteorite to earth is recognized are the displays of light and sound that accompany its fall. These phenomena are widely visible and audible and are, moreover, so startling that many people who have observed them have recorded their observations in writing. Since several hundred meteorite falls have been observed in the last few centuries, eyewitness reports comprise a most voluminous literature. The situation is much less favorable with regard to objective visual records of meteorite falls; for since meteorites arrive without advance warning, a photographic record of a fall has been obtained only recently. The trajectory of the Příbram, Czechoslovakia, stone meteorite (April 7, 1959, 7:30 P.M.) was photographed by two stations 40 kilometers apart. From the photographic records, it has been possible to calculate with great accuracy the orbit of the meteorite prior to its encounter with the earth.

Except in this one instance, all we have available are sketches or paintings prepared after the event on the basis of eyewitness reports. These are often fanciful, and sometimes completely wrong, but in some cases it is evident that the observations were made by skilful and critical observers. Figure 1 shows a typical meteorite fall at Ochansk (Molotov District, U.S.S.R.) on August 30, 1887, at 12:30 P.M. A fiery mass appeared in the sky leaving a luminous train

3

Fig. 1.—Fall of the Ochansk, U.S.S.R., meteorite, August 30, 1887, 12:30 P.M. (After Farrington, *Meteorites,* 1915.)

and clouds of smoke behind it, crossing the sky on a slightly inclined trajectory. The display was visible in the sky for only two to three seconds, and two or three minutes later a noise was heard as if many cannon had been fired. Even the heaviest meteorite that has been observed to fall, that of Sikhote-Alin, in the far east of the U.S.S.R., north of Vladivostok, showed quite similar, though more intense, fall phenomena (Fig. 2). A dazzling bright fireball sped across the sunlit sky for a few seconds. The fireball was bright enough to make the eyes smart. It left a huge smoke trail that was visible for several hours afterward. Soon after the disappearance of the fireball, loud thunderclaps and a rolling noise were heard.

It is scarcely necessary to give further examples of reports of falls. Although the personal element differs, in essence they are all similar to the brief notes above.

If the fall occurs during the day, the intensity of the light is comparable to that of the sun. At night large areas are often so brightly lit that one could read a newspaper without difficulty as the meteorite falls. The fiery path of the meteorite has been observed over very great distances. For example, the passage of the

4

Fig. 2.—Fall of the iron meteorite of Sikhote-Alin, north of Vladivostok, U.S.S.R., February 12, 1947, about 10:38 A.M. (After a painting by P. J. Medvedev, Meteorite Committee, Moscow.)

meteorite of Bath Furnace, Kentucky, in the evening of November 15, 1902, was observed by many people in the states of Louisiana, Mississippi, Alabama, Georgia, Tennessee, and Kentucky, over a distance of nearly 1,000 kilometers.

The point on the trajectory where the meteorite begins to shine is usually most difficult to determine. This is not surprising. Only by accident does an observer ever look into that region of the sky in which the meteorite appears, since most people look skyward only after the light has attracted their attention. The path of the

Pultusk meteorite, which fell in Poland in 1868, was spotted relatively early, at a height of 300 kilometers, whereas that of the Treysa meteorite, which fell in Germany in 1916 in daylight, was noticed only at a height of about 70 to 90 kilometers. Using many such observations, astronomers have calculated the mean height of the starting point of the luminous meteorite trajectory. The value seems to lie in the neighborhood of 150 kilometers.

The apparent direction of the flight path naturally varies with the position of the observer. This is illustrated in Figure 3. The short luminous trail (*AB* in the center of this figure) is the true trajectory of the meteorite plunging vertically to the earth. The small circles, 1, 2, 3, are the positions of three different observers. In order not to confuse the drawing unnecessarily, we have drawn a common vault of the sky, or subjective firmament (the bell-shape or hemisphere of Fig. 3), for all three observers. Actually, a separate sky-vault should have been drawn for each observer, but since they are located so close to each other, the small error involved is negligible. The horizontal circle on which this shared firmament rests represents the horizon, which has also been as-

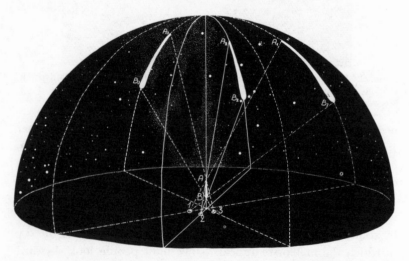

Fig. 3.—True and apparent trajectories of a meteorite.

sumed to be common for all three observers. On the inner part of the rear wall of the hollow hemisphere the Milky Way (stippled) and several constellations are indicated. For example, Orion, with his belt of three stars, is to the right of the Milky Way at B_2. Since the true course of the meteorite is relatively close to the observers, in contrast to the very distant vault of the stars, the three observers see the meteorite path projected on entirely different parts of the sky. Observer 1, for example, sees the path on the extreme right of the sky-vault, running from A_1 to B_1. It lies at the intersection of the plane defined by the two lines of sight $1—A—A_1$ and $1—B—B_1$ with the hemisphere of the sky. The plane that cuts through the hemisphere is marked in the same type of broken line as the corresponding lines of sight. Observer 2, on the other hand, sees the meteorite plummet straight through the constellation of Orion with the end of its path right at the three belt stars, $A_2–B_2$. Finally, for observer 3, the apparent path runs obliquely across the Milky Way from A_3 to B_3. Figure 3 indicates how one can, in principle, reconstruct the true trajectory of the meteorite from several apparent paths. Obviously, the three sky-cutting planes, $1–A_1–B_1$, $2–A_2–B_2$, $3–A_3–B_3$, in which the corresponding apparent paths lie, all intersect at and with the straight line AB. This line of intersection is the true trajectory. The lines of sight through the beginning and end points of the apparent paths likewise intersect at two points, A and B, and these represent the beginning and end points of the true trajectory. In practice, the calculation of a true orbit is of course considerably more difficult, mainly because in the case of a sudden and unexpected phenomenon such as the fall of a meteorite, the determination of apparent paths is subject to large errors.

At the end of the visible path one often observes explosion-like phenomena which usually cause a meteorite to break up into several parts. The point at which this explosion occurs, or at which the light burns out, is called the retardation point. As we shall see, this term was an unfortunate choice. The altitudes of these retardation points can vary quite considerably. The following brief compilation shows several data calculated by astronomers.

TABLE 1

Meteorite	Date of Fall	Terminal Height (in km.)
Homestead, Iowa	Feb. 12, 1875	4
Krähenberg, Germany	May 5, 1869	8
Mocs, Rumania	Feb. 3, 1882	11
Braunau, Czechoslovakia	July 14, 1847	15
Treysa, Germany	Apr. 3, 1916	16
Orgueil, France	May 14, 1864	23
Pultusk, Poland	Jan. 30, 1868	42

From these figures it can be seen that the visible tracks occasionally descend into the troposphere (the lower part of our atmosphere which ends at about 12 kilometers altitude). Frequently, however, they end while still well up in the stratosphere (above 12 km.).

The path of the meteorite is usually described as perfectly straight or only slightly curved, but exceptions occur. The stone meteorite of Prambachkirchen, in Austria (fell November 5, 1932), broke in two at an altitude of 14 kilometers. The smaller of these two parts, with a final weight of 2 kilograms, moved in a circular arc of 10-kilometer radius, thereby changing its direction by more than 180 degrees.

The color of the light varies. Usually it is described as white, but occasionally also as greenish, reddish, or yellow. The color is different at different stages of the flight path. This cannot be ascribed to differences in the composition of the atmosphere at various heights, since we know from other observations (e.g., spectrum analysis of the aurora borealis) that nitrogen and oxygen are the principal constituents of the atmosphere up to the highest altitudes. Examination of the rather limited number of meteor spectra shows that the line spectra characteristic of luminous gases predominate. The following elements were detected with certainty: iron, nickel, calcium, magnesium, manganese, chromium, silicon, sodium, and, with less certainty, aluminum. Occasionally sudden outbursts of light have been observed, and, when these do occur, they are often multiple. Figure 4 shows three such sudden light outbursts of a bright meteor of July 26, 1952. The figure shows plainly that the diameter of the light source does not increase, but

Fig. 4.—Multiple flare-ups of a meteor, July 26, 1952, 12:08 A.M. (Photograph of the Sonneberg Observatory, Germany, by A. Ahnert.)

only the intensity. Sometimes the light intensity rises quite suddenly when the meteorite enters the lower, denser parts of the atmosphere where the resistance of the air is considerably greater than in the very tenuous upper strata. For example, the very well-observed path of the Pultusk meteorite, mentioned above, at first (altitude about 300 km.) merely resembled that of a shooting star. At a height of about 180 kilometers, the light intensity increased greatly and the color changed to bluish-green. In the lowest portion of the path the intensity increased further and the color tended toward red.

The light comes from a luminous gas cloud, usually round or pear-shaped. This cloud has an apparent size far greater than that of the meteorite itself. This peculiar discrepancy in the size of the meteorite and the fireball had already been noticed by the ancients. The well-known physicist, Chladni, who also happened to be the first man to convince the scientific world of the cosmic origin of meteorites, said: "As already pointed out by Plutarch in the case of the stone fall near Aegos-Potamos, the size of the fireball is always much greater than the volume of the subsequently fallen bodies." Whenever sufficient observations by eyewitnesses existed to permit a calculation of the diameter of the fireballs, sizes of no less than a few hundred meters were usually obtained. A most conservative estimate for the Pultusk meteorite gave a diameter of 300 meters. In the case of the Treysa meteorite the apparent diameter at its time of maximum luminosity at 50-kilometer altitude was 1,000 meters, which gradually fell to about 400 meters toward the end of the trajectory. Yet the largest diameter of the Treysa meteorite is only 36 centimeters! (In concrete terms, the flare was bigger than a football stadium, but the meteorite itself only the size of the football!) It should be noted, however, that these calculated diameters of the fireballs are, for the most part, due to an overexposure effect that can lead to an increase in the apparent size for both the eye and the photographic plate.

The interpretation of the light phenomena is most difficult, both qualitatively and quantitatively, and has not been satisfactorily worked out so far. For one thing, a major difficulty comes from the fact that we cannot yet study the problem experimentally—after all, velocities of tens of kilometers per second are involved, so that calculations have to depend to a very large degree on extrapolations. A further difficulty comes from the fact that during the flight of the meteorite through the atmosphere its speed and mass, as well as the density of the atmosphere, change continuously. So far, we have found out that in the highest, thinnest parts of the atmosphere the light is caused at least partly by luminescence, or cold emission, coming from the collisions of individual air molecules with the meteorite. In the lower regions of the atmosphere thermal emission of light also seems to play a part.

About half of the bright train of the falling meteorite is caused by air molecules that are ionized upon collision with the meteorite.

As we know, every atom consists of a positively charged nucleus and a shell of electrons—tiny particles of negative charge. In collisions of sufficient force, one or several electrons of an atom can be knocked out of the atom, and the atom is then said to be "ionized." The ionized atom attracts free electrons to fill up the vacancies in its electron shell and it therefore captures some of those present in the surrounding space. In this process, light is given off (recombination glow). Depending on the speed of the recombination, the luminosity of the train can last for varying lengths of time: the more free electrons available, the faster the ions will be used up. Usually the time is very short: one, or only a few seconds; but in some cases a glow of about 45 minutes (e.g., in the case of the Pasamonte, New Mexico meteorite) and longer has been observed. In these cases, the prolonged glow may be due to "excited states" of the atoms or molecules formed by recombination, or to chemical reactions of unstable substances that can be abundant at high altitudes, e.g., nitric oxide.

Daytime meteorite falls are often accompanied by a smoke trail of very finely divided meteorite material. Upon penetrating the atmosphere, the meteorite collides with the air molecules in its way. Apart from the ionization discussed above, these collisions cause a very rapid and intense heating of the outermost layer of the meteorite to well above its melting point. The white-hot molten material is stripped off, or swept off, and dispersed very finely. It then forms the smoke trail (see Fig. 1, p. 4, extreme upper left). A very considerable part of the original mass of the meteorite, before its descent into the atmosphere, is dispersed by this violent process, and the meteorites found after the fall are often only small residues of the original body. For example, Soviet scientists estimate that no less than 200 tons of meteoritic matter were contained in the smoke trail of the large meteorite iron shower of Sikhote-Alin, halfway between Vladivostok and Chabarovsk (February 12, 1947). A smoke trail (Fig. 2) remained in the sky for several hours and was so dense that the sun was either completely obscured, or was seen only as a faintly glowing red disk. The solid body remaining was

11

estimated to be only about 70 tons. When larger particles of the meteorite are spalled off they cause glowing sparks and explosive light displays.

SOUND

Even more impressive and frightening than these conspicuous light phenomena are the sounds that come with meteorite falls. Indeed, they are so terrifying that people have fallen down in terror or have run away and sought cover in buildings or under trees. Animals, too, are similarly affected. Horses bolt; dogs tuck their tails under and hide. Depending on the position of the observer, a whole scale of sounds can be observed, from a thunder-like stroke that shakes the windows to the boom of cannon, from rifle fire down to sounds like the clatter of wagon wheels. Roaring and hissing noises are also reported frequently. An interesting point is that many observers claim to have heard a hissing noise during the descent of the meteorite. The trajectory of the meteorite is so far away from the observer that simultaneous observation of the moving fireball and a sound phenomenon produced by it is not likely. If this is self-deception on the part of these observers, it is probably based on an unconscious recall of those objects that have the greatest resemblance to fireballs, namely skyrockets and Roman candles. People watching fireworks usually stand close enough to be able to hear a hissing noise at the same time as they see the display.

Certain delusions are common among technically untrained observers of meteorite falls. Absurd statements are often made about the place of fall. In most cases the meteorite is supposed to have fallen quite close to the observer, only a few hundred meters away, or in the next valley. On the following day the man goes to the field or meadow that he believes to be the place of fall and picks up some peculiar looking stone, or fragment of a plow, or something similar that he had not previously noticed. He thinks, of course, that he has found a meteorite, although the real one may have fallen perhaps 10 or even 100 kilometers away. These self-deceptions are caused in part by the suddenness and spectacular nature of the fall and also by the lack of nearby landmarks in the sky

12

FIG. 5.—Range of audibility and visibility of the meteorite of Treysa, Germany, April 3, 1916. Sound phenomena were heard at the localities indicated by solid circles, but were not heard at the points indicated by open circles. (After A. Wegener, in *Schriften d. Ges. z. Beförd. d. ges. Naturwiss.*, Marburg, 1917.)

itself. The moon and the stars, familiar images in the night sky, follow their courses silently and with but faint light, and we know that they are quite far away from the earth. By contrast, the fire-

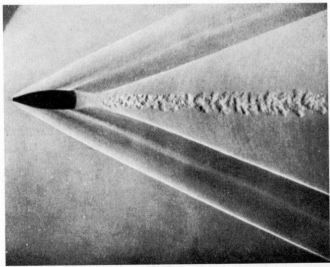

FIG. 6.—Shock wave of a rifle bullet. (After P. P. Ewald, *Kristalle und Röntgenstrahlen*, 1929.)

FIG. 7.—Shock waves of splinters torn loose by the bullet. (After P. P. Ewald.)

ball traveling with a brilliant glare and thundering roar gives the impression of being very close.

The sounds of falling meteorites can be heard over very large areas. Where investigations were made, audibility zones were found to be of 60 to 70 kilometers radius and greater. Just as in the case of artillery fire, one sometimes observes several distinct zones of audibility (separated by zones of silence). For example, in the Treysa meteorite fall mentioned previously, the inner zone of audibility had a radius of about 60 kilometers, whereas further sound phenomena were heard at a distance of 95 and 120 kilometers, as shown in Figure 5. This is a well-known effect of the refraction and reflection of sound in our atmosphere.

The origin of the sound phenomena has been explained experimentally. For the meteorites, the same causes should operate as for high speed bullets. Figure 6 shows a photograph of a high speed rifle bullet in flight. We can see plainly that a conical shock wave, the so-called head wave, originates at the tip of the bullet. This head wave is responsible for the thunder-like clap, completely analogous to the "sonic boom" of supersonic aircraft. The rolling noises of various kinds are in turn produced by the turbulence behind the bullet as well as by reflection of sound waves on clouds and from the surface of the earth. Figure 7 explains the origin of the machine-gun-like rattle reported by many observers. The bullet has just penetrated a wooden board to the right of the picture and has therefore been slightly deflected from its path. However, while penetrating the board, it has torn off a number of wooden splinters and given them supersonic velocities. Each splinter now produces its own head wave and the combined effect of all these head waves is the clattering sound. In the case of the meteorite the same effects will be produced by many small fragments broken from the main mass during flight.

IMPACT

Conspicuous and impressive as the light and sound phenomena may be, the effects produced by the meteorite on impact at the solid surface of the earth are amazingly slight. Table 2 summarizes the observational material. In addition to the weight of the meteorite, the depths of penetration and the type of soil are listed.

Figure 8 shows the impact point of the meteorite from Bjurböle, Finland. It is one of the largest stone meteorites (these are meteorites that consist primarily of stony materials) and fell on the ice cover of a frozen bay. The heaviest stone meteorite whose fall has been observed (March 18, 1948) is that of Norton County, Kansas. It made a hole 3 meters deep. Figure 9, representing that of the St. Michel I meteorite (also from Finland) shows how inconspicuous the impact hole of a small meteorite can be. The holes are usually round and either go straight downward or show only small deviations from the vertical. For example, the meteorite of Knyahinya had an impact hole that was inclined only 27 degrees from the vertical. During its impact, pieces of soil were thrown distances up to 50 meters. The impact effects are very slight, even in the case of the iron meteorites (these consist largely of metallic

15

TABLE 2

Name of Meteorite	Date of Fall	Weight (in Kg.)	Penetration Depth (in meters)	Kind of Soil
Lumpkin, Ga. (U.S.A.) ...	Oct. 6, 1869	0.4	0.25	Trodden dirt in farmyard
Gnadenfrei, Silesia	May 17, 1879	1.0	0.30	Loose soil
Ibbenbüren, Germany ...	June 17, 1870	2.0	0.70	Footpath
St. Michel I, Finland	July 12, 1910	7.0	0.59	10 cm. soil overlying glacial till
Bandong, Java	Dec. 10, 1871	8.0	1.00	Rice paddy
St. Michel II, Finland	July 12, 1910	10.0	0.50	Moraine
Hvittis, Finland	Oct. 21, 1901	14.0	0.60	Soil
Tjabé, Java	Sept. 19, 1869	20.0	0.60	Field
Braunau, Czechoslovakia..	July 14, 1847	23.6	1.00	Field bank
Mocs, Rumania	Feb. 3, 1882	36.0	0.66	Frozen ground
Lancé, France	July 23, 1872	47.0	1.40	Soil
Kernouvé, France	May 22, 1869	80.00	1.00	Meadow
Ensisheim, Alsace	Nov. 16, 1492	127.0	1.50	....
Treysa, Germany	Apr. 3, 1916	63.28	1.60	.75 m. loose forest soil and loess clay, 85 cm. soft, clayey sandstone
Knyahinya, U.S.S.R.	June 9, 1866	234.0	3.30	Damp meadow
Bjurböle, Finland	Mar. 12, 1899	330.0	6.00	0.40 m. ice, 0.50 m. water, 6.0 m. soft mud and gray clay
Paragould, Ark.	Feb. 17, 1930	352.0	2.50	....
Norton County, Kans. ...	Aug. 18, 1948	1000.0	3.00	Soil
Sikhote-Alin, Siberia	Feb. 12, 1947	1754.0	3.2	Platelike shape; soft ground overlying solid rock
Sikhote-Alin, Siberia	Feb. 12, 1947	255.6	8.0	Oblong, pointed shape

nickel-iron), despite their frequently much higher weight. For example, the 60-ton meteorite from the Hoba farm near Grootfontain, South West Africa, the heaviest of all known meteorites, imbedded itself in friable limestone at a depth of only 1.5 meters. The iron meteorites of Cape York in Greenland, weighing up to 30.875 tons, lay on solid gneiss rock, or were barely imbedded in moraine rubble, without any trace of an impact. Here we may guess that they fell on a thick layer of ice or snow and sank to their final location as the snow or ice melted. The largest individual iron left unbroken in the meteorite shower of Sikhote-Alin, Eastern

FIG. 8.—Impact hole of the meteorite of Bjurböle, Finland, March 12, 1899. (After Ramsay, in *Bull. de la Comm. Géolog. de Finlande*, No. 12.)

Siberia (February 12, 1947), having a weight of 1.754 tons, was found in a small funnel-shaped pit at a depth of 4 meters. The larger blocks of this shower produced impact scars of diameter up to 26.5 meters and were shattered completely in the process. Figure

FIG. 9.—Impact hole of the meteorite of St. Michel, Finland, July 12, 1910. (After Borgström, in *Bull. de la Comm. Géolog. de Finlande*, No. 34.)

10 shows the inner slope of the largest conical pit (mean diameter 26.5 meters, depth 6.0 meters).

Fig. 10.—Interior view facing north of the largest impact pit of the iron meteorite shower Sikhote-Alin, February 12, 1947. Diameter 26.5 meters, depth 6 meters. (Photograph by E. Krinov.)

The observational material just presented, which could easily be augmented by many additional examples, is rather surprising in some respects. That the nature of the ground should have an influence on the impact effects is easily understood, of course. The harder the ground, the smaller the effects. When striking solid rock, meteorites, particularly stone meteorites, are usually completely shattered without leaving the slightest impact traces.

What *is* surprising, on the other hand, is the fact that the impact effects are so slight. After all, we noted above that meteorites enter the atmosphere with velocities of many kilometers per second, velocities that far exceed those of the fastest bullet; yet their effects are far less than those of dud shells from medium-caliber cannon. Moreover, when a larger body of material is reviewed, it becomes apparent that for a given type of soil, the intensity of the effect seems to increase only with the mass of the meteorite, being about the same for equal masses, although the initial velocity varies greatly from meteorite to meteorite (lying in the range of 15 to 45 kilometers per second, and conceivably up to twice that velocity). The reason for this peculiar behavior is the atmosphere, which, in spite of its "airy" consistency, constitutes a protective armor against missiles from outer space.

In order to understand the influence of the atmosphere, we must turn to childhood memories and some elementary physics. When we throw a solid object, such as a rock, its effect on striking the target depends on its impetus, or kinetic energy. It is hardly possible to break a window with a pea, but it is easy if we replace it with a stone the size of a nut and throw it with the same velocity. The energy of the missile obviously depends on its mass.

Further, if we throw the stone as slowly as possible, the window pane may only crack. On the other hand, if we throw the same stone with all our strength, the window pane shatters with a crash. Physicists have examined these relations and found that they can be described by a very simple equation. Let us represent the kinetic energy with the letter E, the mass with m, and the velocity with v. Then, these three quantities are related by the familiar expression:

$$E = \frac{1}{2} mv^2.$$

From this simple equation, we can easily derive, in a qualitative sense at least, our childhood observations. For example, if we double the mass of our projectile, the equation tells us that the kinetic energy will become twice as large (if the velocity remains constant). The original numerical value of m is now doubled. Consequently, the numerical value of E must also become twice as large. Doubling the velocity, however, is another matter. In our equation, v enters to the second power, that is, the kinetic energy increases much more rapidly with the velocity than it does with the mass. If, for example, the velocity is 10 meters per second, then the numerical value for v^2 is obviously $10^2 = 100$. If we double the velocity to 20 meters per second, keeping the mass constant, then the numerical value is not 200, but $20^2 = 400$. The value for E has increased fourfold. At a threefold increase in velocity, it increases ninefold, etc.

Let us now return to meteorites. We saw that those of equal mass penetrated to about the same depth in the same type of soil. This implies, according to our equation, that they also had about the same velocity when they hit the earth, although they might well have entered the earth's atmosphere with very different velocities. Hence, the atmosphere not only slows the meteorites greatly, but also has an equalizing effect on their entry velocities. A quick review of the factors that determine the air resistance of flying bodies enables us to understand this effect. The amount of air resistance is dependent not only on the cross-section, the shape of the body, and several other things that are only of relatively minor importance in this connection, but also on the velocity. By way of example, if we take a leisurely walk on a windless day we feel very little air resistance. On the other hand, if we get on a motorcycle and take off at 100 kilometers per hour, we feel a strong pressure on our bodies; the air resistance has become something that can be felt. To accelerate from 90 to 100 kilometers per hour, we have to give the engine considerably more gas than in increasing the speed from 20 to 30 kilometers per hour. This is only a crudely qualitative indication, but clear enough nonetheless, of the fact that air resistance does not simply increase with the first power of the velocity, but, just as in the equation for the kinetic energy, goes up much more sharply.

Ballistic and gas kinetic investigations have shown that once the velocity of sound is exceeded (300 m/sec. in air at sea level), the velocity enters to the second power in the equation for air resistance. The conclusion that we can draw from this is that meteorites of very high velocity will be decelerated much more strongly by the atmosphere than those with a low velocity.

A quantitative calculation of the deceleration of a meteorite in its flight through the atmosphere can be done only by means of an equation too complicated to discuss here. We must keep in mind that not only the velocity, but also the mass of the meteorite decrease during flight and that the density of the atmosphere increases at the same time. For this reason, we need only present a few results of this calculation in tabular and graphic form. In

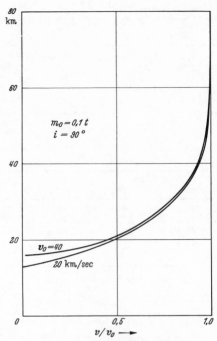

Fig. 11.—Deceleration of two iron meteorites of initial mass 0.1 tons, vertical incidence, and initial velocities of 20 and 40 kilometers per second, respectively; v/v_0 = ratio of velocity at altitude v to the initial velocity v_0.

Tables 3 and 4 we show the deceleration of iron meteorites of different initial masses (m_0) and with two different entry velocities (v_0) and entry angles (i). In the first column we have given the altitude in kilometers (h) to which these numbers apply.

In Figure 11 we have plotted the deceleration of two iron meteorites of 100 kilograms initial mass and an entry angle of 90°. The entry velocities are 40 kilometers per second (upper curve) and 20 kilometers per second (lower curve). These curves show that the meteorite with the lower entry velocity plunges deeper into our atmosphere than that with the higher velocity, a result that is at first baffling. At oblique entry angles the deceleration is even more pronounced. At altitudes of 16 and 13 kilometers, respectively, the cosmic velocity has dropped to zero, and both meteorites

21

TABLE 3 *

i h (km)	$m_0 = 0.1$ t		1 t		10 t		100 t		1000 t	
	90⁰	45⁰	90⁰	45⁰	90⁰	45⁰	90⁰	45⁰	90⁰	45⁰
80	20.0	20.0	20.0	20.0	20.0	20.0	20.0	20.0	20.0	20.0
60	19.9	19.8	19.9	19.9	20.0	20.0	20.0	20.0	20.0	20.0
40	18.7	18.1	19.4	19.1	19.7	19.6	19.8	19.7	19.9	19.8
20	9.7	7.4	14.5	12.6	17.1	16.1	18.7	18.1	19.3	19.1
0	—	—	—	—	4.3	2.2	9.8	7.4	14.5	12.6

* $v_0 = 20$ km/sec

TABLE 4 *

i h (km)	$m_0 = 0.1$ t		1 t		10 t		100 t		1000 t	
	90⁰	45⁰	90⁰	45⁰	90⁰	45⁰	90⁰	45⁰	90⁰	45⁰
80	39.9	39.8	39.9	39.9	39.9	39.9	39.9	39.9	39.9	39.9
60	39.7	39.6	39.8	39.8	39.8	39.8	39.9	39.9	39.9	39.9
40	37.2	36.1	38.7	38.2	39.3	39.0	39.7	39.6	39.8	39.8
20	18.7	13.3	28.5	24.5	34.2	32.1	37.7	36.1	38.7	38.2
0	—	—	—	—	2.3	1.1	18.7	13.3	28.5	24.5

* $v_0 = 40$ km/sec

now continue their path only under the mutually counteracting influences of the earth's gravity and air resistance. Their speed reaches a constant value and does not decrease any further. The altitude at which cosmic velocity is completely lost is often called the "point of retardation." This term is poorly chosen inasmuch as it gives the false impression that the meteorite stands still for a moment. The constant terminal velocity with which the meteorite now falls to earth is very small compared to its entry velocity, so small, in fact, that it is no longer enough to produce a luminous cloud of gas, or to melt the meteorite on the surface by air friction. The light phenomena, therefore, cease at this "point of retardation." Observers who found themselves close enough to the point of impact then saw the meteorites fall as dark bodies.

This conclusion, namely, that the impact velocity of meteorites of normal size is quite small and about the same for meteorites of equal mass, has been confirmed in a number of cases where ballistics experts were able to estimate the impact velocity from the appearance of the impact holes. Some calculated velocities are: Middlesbrough, England (March 14, 1881), 126 meters per second;

Shelburne, Canada (August 13, 1904), 157 meters per second; St. Michel II, Finland (July 12, 1910), 169 meters per second; Hvittis, Finland (October 21, 1901), 178 meters per second; and St. Michel I (Finland), 213 meters per second.

One important qualification should be made to all these considerations and calculations: they are valid only for meteorites of the mass that we have found to arrive on the earth thus far. For extremely large meteorites the situation changes very considerably in a quantitative sense. In the section on giant meteorites this point is discussed in more detail and the figures in the last four columns of Tables 3 and 4 are explained.

The behavior of meteorites differs from what the fall phenomena might lead one to believe in still another respect. As we saw, the surface of the meteorite is heated to the melting point by collisions with air molecules. Nonetheless, the main mass of the meteorite is not heated appreciably by this process. This is shown by direct observation. Stone meteorites picked up immediately after the fall were, in many cases, no more than lukewarm. Some of them struck haystacks or barns without causing fires to break out in the easily combustible materials. In other cases, too, no sign of burning could be observed at the impact points. Only the meteorite of Alfianello, Italy (February 16, 1883), is alleged to have singed the grass slightly. Iron meteorites, on the other hand, are occasionally claimed to have been hot. For example, the iron meteorite of Braunau, Czechoslovakia (July 14, 1847), was too hot to touch as late as six hours after the fall, although another block of the same iron which struck the roof of a building, failed to singe the straw thatch noticeably. No meteorite, not even an iron, has ever caused a fire.

Moreover, the internal structure of a meteorite provides a rather sensitive indicator of reheating after its formation. In by far the greatest number of cases, it turns out that the meteorite as a whole was not heated much in its flight through the atmosphere, certainly not to the melting point. Where such reheating could be established, the "heat-affected zone" (see below) was only a few millimeters thick. The reason for this is that the reheating was of very short duration. There is not enough time for the heat to spread to the interior of the meteorite since the reheating lasts for only a few seconds at any one spot. Any part of the meteorite heated for a longer time is melted and swept away. This seems somewhat surprising, at least for the iron meteorites, since we know from practical experience how good a heat-conductor iron is. But this finding can be confirmed experimentally: if an iron ball about the size of a man's head is exposed to the full flame of an acetylene torch for a few seconds, the surface may melt but the interior of the ball remains cold. In the last part of its path, when the meteorite travels with a uniform and relatively low velocity, the air acts only as a cooling agent, much as in the case of aircraft or automobile engines. In this manner, even such of the outermost fused layer as has not been stripped off has been cooled considerably by the time the meteorite reaches the earth.

The entire loss of energy due to the light and sound phenomena and the ablation is at the expense of the kinetic energy and mass of the meteorite. Tables 5 and 6 show the loss of mass suffered by two meteorites of different entry velocities and different angles of inclination under otherwise identical conditions, in much the same way as Tables 3 and 4 show the loss of velocity.

Let us first consider only the meteorite with an initial mass of

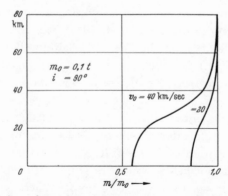

FIG. 12.—Mass loss of two iron meteorites of initial mass 0.1 tons, vertical incidence, and initial velocity 20 and 40 kilometers per second; m/m_0 = ratio of mass m at the altitude in question to the initial mass, m_0.

100 kilograms. From these tables and from Figure 12 it is evident that the loss of mass is much greater at the higher than at the lower entry velocity. At an entry velocity of 40 kilometers per second the residual mass weighs only 55 kilograms compared to 86 kilograms for 20 kilometers per second. This has an important bearing on the possibility that cosmic bodies might reach the surface of the earth as easily detectable objects. We shall return to this question later on, and shall then discuss the figures in the last four columns of Tables 5 and 6.

METEORITE SHOWERS

These relatively slight impact effects are not enhanced appreciably if a large cluster of meteorites falls instead of a single chunk. These are called meteorite showers or meteorite swarms. The number of meteorites in such showers differs very greatly, ranging from 2–3, through 20–40, up to many thousands. For the meteorite shower of L'Aigle, France (April 26, 1803), the number was estimated as 2,000 to 3,000. For the Holbrook, Arizona, shower (July 9, 1912), 14,000; for that of Mocs, Rumania (February 3, 1882), 3000, or

TABLE 5 *

i h (km)	$m_0 =$ 100 kg		1 t		10 t		100 t		1000 t	
	90^0	45^0	90^0	45^0	90^0	45^0	90^0	45^0	90^0	45^0
80	100	100	1.00	1.00	10.0	10.0	100	100	1000	1000
60	100	100	1.00	1.00	10.0	10.0	100	100	1000	1000
40	98	97	0.99	0.99	10.0	9.95	100	100	1000	1000
20	90	89	0.93	0.91	9.6	9.5	98	97	990	990
0	86	86	0.86	0.86	8.7	8.7	90	89	930	910

* $v_0 = 20$ km/sec

TABLE 6 *

i h (km)	$m_0 =$ 100 kg		1 t		10 t		100 t		1000 t	
	90^0	45^0	90^0	45^0	90^0	45^0	90^0	45^0	90^0	45^0
80	100	100	1.00	1.00	10.0	10.0	100	100	1000	1000
60	99	99	0.99	0.99	10.0	10.0	100	100	1000	1000
40	92	90	0.96	0.95	9.8	9.7	99	99	990	990
20	63	59	0.75	0.68	8.6	8.1	92	90	960	950
0	55	55	0.55	0.55	5.5	5.5	63	59	750	680

* $v_0 = 40$ km/sec

according to another author, 100,000. For that of Pultusk, Poland (January 30, 1868), again about 100,000. All the above falls refer to stones. In the case of irons, showers are less frequent and involve a smaller number of pieces. Some such showers are the finds of Mukerop, South West Africa, of which more than 50 pieces have been found, often of considerable size. The irons of Toluca, Mexico, and Coahuila, Mexico, which are rather widely distributed in collections, also represent iron meteorite showers.

A few years ago, on February 12, 1947, the fall of such a hail of iron was observed for the first time near Sikhote-Alin, eastern Siberia. Altogether some 23 tons of iron meteorites were found, mostly in larger pieces. The heaviest mass found weighs 1.745 tons. There must have been larger masses, estimated to have weighed some 20 to 30 tons, but they shattered completely into minute splinters on impact. The total mass of the shower has been estimated as about 70 tons and the impact area as about 1.6 square kilometers.

The individual meteorites in a shower are usually distributed over an elliptical area as shown in Figure 13 for the meteorite shower of Homestead, Iowa. The long axis of the ellipse is about 10 kilometers, the short axis about 5 kilometers. The flight direc-

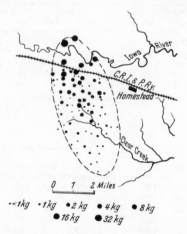

Fig. 13.—Fall area of the meteorite shower of Homestead, Iowa, February 12, 1875. (After Farrington.)

tion of this shower was from south to north. For an oblique entry angle the heavier pieces of such a shower, according to the equation for the kinetic energy discussed above, must fly somewhat farther than the lighter ones, since their kinetic energy is substantially larger, owing to larger mass. As a result, the largest individuals are found at the northern end of the ellipse. More than a hundred stones were found all told, the heaviest weighing about 32 kilograms. Table 7 lists a number of meteorite showers, with the dimensions of each fall area, the number of individuals, and the total weight.

TABLE 7

Place and Date of Fall	Extent of Fall Area (in km.)	No. of Fragments	Total Weight (in kg.)
Holbrook, Arizona July 19, 1912	4.5 × 0.9	ca. 14,000	ca. 218
Pultusk, Poland Jan. 1, 1868	8 × 1.5	ca. 100,000	....
Homestead, Iowa Feb. 12, 1875	10 × 5	more than 100	ca. 230
L'Aigle, France April 26, 1803	12 × 4	2,000–3,000	ca. 40
Stannern, Czechoslovakia May 22, 1808	13 × 4.5	200–300	ca. 52
Mocs, Rumania Feb. 3, 1882	14.5 × 3	more than 3,000	ca. 300
Knyahinya, U.S.S.R. June 9, 1866	14.5 × 4.5	more than 1,000	ca. 500
Hessle, Sweden Jan. 1, 1869	16 × 4.5	....	ca. 23
Khairpur, India Sept. 23, 1873	25 × 4.5	many stones	....
Sikhote-Alin, Siberia Feb. 12, 1947	2.1 × 1.04	many masses & fragments	ca. 70,000

From the surface features (see p. 83) of the individual pieces from such a shower, one can infer, in the case of some showers at least, that they entered the atmosphere as already separated objects. In other cases, on the basis of differences in the degree of ablation of the individual stones, it appears that most of them were formed by breakup in the atmosphere.

METEORITE CRATERS

Our observations up to this point have shown us that the impact effects of meteorites of the size that we encounter on the earth are remarkably small. But we may remind ourselves that the surface of the earth bears a number of most peculiar structures of crater-like appearance. These structures are usually much alike and several of them have been investigated quite thoroughly. These researches have led to the conclusion that a number of these structures can be interpreted only as impact sites of meteorites—impact sites that enormously exceed everything discussed up till now. These craters have been called "meteorite craters." Their colossal dimensions imply the impact of meteorites so huge in size as to be unknown to us on earth during recorded history. The problem of their origin is not only of interest to scientists, but is important to the whole human race. If such a giant meteorite falls in a densely populated region, it would cause a catastrophe of unimaginable extent. If it should happen to strike a major city, such as Berlin, Paris, London or Los Angeles, nothing would be left of it, and there would be no survivors.

For a long time, only one of these meteorite craters, that of Arizona, was known. D. M. Barringer was the first to recognize its meteoritic nature, but because of its uniqueness its meteoritic origin was repeatedly questioned. In recent years, however, many similar craters have been discovered, and it is certain for most of them that they represent the impact sites of gigantic meteorites. And in 1908 nature did us the dubious favor of demonstrating to us, ad oculos, the impact of such a giant meteorite in Siberia. There can no longer be any doubt that meteorites of vastly greater size and velocity than normally observed occasionally strike the earth, although the main masses of the projectiles that made these gigantic holes have not been found in any of these cases. This represents another very remarkable property of meteorite craters which we shall discuss later on.

FIG. 14.—Geographic distribution of the meteorite craters. The numbers are discussed in the text.

Fig. 15.—Meteorite crater of Canyon Diablo, Arizona. *Top picture:* crater outline superimposed on an aerial photograph of the southern tip of Manhattan Island. (Photograph by H. Armstrong Roberts, Philadelphia). *Bottom picture:* aerial photograph of the Arizona crater. (Photograph by the American Meteorite Laboratory.)

The map in Fig. 14 shows the locations of all known craters for which a meteoritic nature is either certain (solid points) or probable (open points). The numbers will be discussed later in the text. This map shows that these craters are located, with few exceptions, in unpopulated desert regions.

The longest known and best studied meteorite crater is that of Canyon Diablo in Arizona (No. 1 on the map). The lower half of Figure 15 shows an aerial photograph of this structure. The crater lies in an arid and completely level plain consisting of a

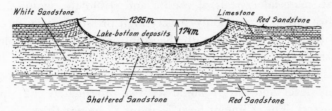

FIG. 16.—Cross-section of the Arizona meteor crater. (After *National Geographic Magazine*, 1928.)

surface layer of limestone underlain by white and red sandstone. Its outline is approximately circular (or square with rounded corners). Its maximum diameter is 1,295 meters, and its present depth, measured from the rim, 174 meters. An idea of its size is given by the aerial photograph of downtown Manhattan in the upper half of Figure 15, over which the outline of the crater has been drawn to scale. The rim of the crater consists in part of distorted beds of rock and partly of loose fragments of material from the crater. These fragments vary in size from rock flour up to boulders of some 4,000 tons. Figure 17 shows such an oversized boulder, the hugeness of which becomes apparent by comparison with the horse in the same picture. The inner structure of the crater is shown in Figure 16. The sandstone underlying the crater floor has been thoroughly crushed to great depth, and it crumbles to dust in the hand under gentle pressure. Some is sintered and fused, and

FIG. 17.—Limestone block thrown out of the crater of Canyon Diablo. (After a photograph by the United States Geological Survey.)

31

in this material crystals of coesite and stishovite, modifications of silica (SiO_2) formed only at very high pressures, have recently been found. At greater depth the sandstone beds are completely undisturbed, a point of great significance. The crater floor itself consists of the sediments of a small lake, now dried out. It is completely level and covers an area of approximately 1.2 square kilometers. The sediment layer is about 27 meters thick.

No definite statement can be made about the age of the crater. A cedar growing on its wall is 700 years old, and so the crater must be older. From the degree of weathering of the limestone, some geologists have concluded that it is not older than 5,000 years. It is thus possible that the fall of the giant meteorite was observed by the local Indians. Three of their legends concern the crater.* According to them, one of their gods came down from the sky, accompanied by thunder and lightning, and buried himself at this spot. Even today, Indians still following tribal customs are not permitted to visit the crater; it is considered taboo. It is also significant that Indians did not participate in the search for meteoritic iron in the crater vicinity. However, other age estimates give much higher values, up to 50,000 years.

But where then is the giant projectile that made this hole? Large amounts of iron meteorite fragments, totaling about 30 tons in weight, have been found in the vicinity of the crater during the last century, though not in the crater itself. These chunks of meteoritic iron were mixed with the rock material thrown from the crater. The map in Figure 18 shows the exact location of the crater as well as the points at which many of the meteorites were found. Along with the metallic nickel-iron, one finds large amounts of a solid rust-brown material consisting mostly of oxides of iron and nickel mixed with calcareous substances and other terrestrial materials. Because of the layered structure often exhibited by this material, it has been called "iron shale." It was believed formerly

---

*[J. D. Buddhue has expressed doubts of the authenticity of these legends. None of the Indian tribes now living in northern Arizona were there when the crater was formed, and no such legends are found in the available literature on Hopi, Navajo, and Pueblo mythology.—Translator]

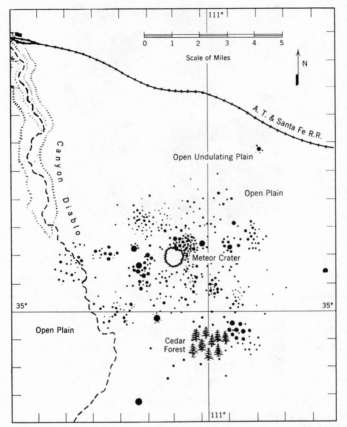

FIG. 18.—Distribution of the Canyon Diablo meteorites around Meteor Crater, Arizona. (Courtesy the American Museum of Natural History.)

that it represented a weathering product of the limestone, but its chemical composition, and the structure of specimens such as the one shown in Figure 19, show that this iron shale is closely related to the meteoritic iron. In the piece illustrated, the center consists of metal and the outer shell is iron shale. Since the Canyon Diablo iron is very resistant to weathering, and since many blocks of meteoritic iron were found without this crust, this oxidized material can hardly be a weathering product but was probably formed during the fall of the giant meteorite. It is significant in this con-

Fɪɢ. 19.—Meteoritic iron with iron shale from Canyon Diablo. (After Merrill, in *U.S. National Museum Bulletin 94.*)

nection that this iron shale is found at all definitely identified meteorite craters, while it is missing in the cases of all but the heaviest common meteorites.

But the few tons of all this meteoritic material added together are of course far from sufficient to open up such a gigantic hole. Recent estimates suggest that a projectile about 20 meters across weighing 10,000 to 100,000 million tons would be necessary. If such a mass were still present at the bottom of the crater, then this would represent not only a deposit of millions of tons of metallic iron but also hundreds of thousands of tons of nickel as well as cobalt and metals of the platinum group in appreciable quantities. Thus it would be an object of great economic as well as scientific value. In fact, the thorough and expensive mining investigation of the crater was motivated primarily by economic considerations. About thirty drill-holes and shafts, some of them of great depth, were sunk in from the crater floor. These have added greatly to our knowledge of the structure of the crater but did not lead to the discovery of the giant meteorite. After this failure, it was assumed that the meteorite had traveled in an oblique trajectory from the north and therefore was not located under the crater floor but under the southern rim. Another hole was drilled at this point, touched some iron shale at depth, and finally, at 420 meters, the drill jammed. A new corporation was founded and started at once to dig a shaft outside the crater in order to reach the suspected meteorite. However, at a depth of about 200 meters, the shaft flooded. This failure ended the project, the last part of which alone had cost roughly half a million dollars. In 1930, a thorough geophysical study was undertaken after earlier magnetic investigations had failed to locate the projectile. These new studies only indicated that some iron-containing material is deeply buried in the southwest quadrant of the crater. We shall see later that finding the main mass of the meteorite is most improbable.

All these mining attempts have established one point with certainty: that this crater was formed by the impact of a meteorite. The type of rock—sedimentary rocks, not a a trace of igneous rocks were found—the undisturbed character of the deep-lying beds, the sintered sandstone with coesite and stishovite, and the intimate mixture of meteoritic material with the rock debris on the crater rim, rule out a volcanic origin such as maars.* Other purely terrestrial modes of origin, such as doline formation,† or a salt dome pushed up from greater depth by geologic forces only to be dissolved by surface water, or, finally, the explosion of natural gas, are ruled out for the above reasons.

The controversy about the nature of the Canyon Diablo crater was still in full force when another similar structure was discovered at Odessa, Texas in 1928 (No. 2 on the map). Although this crater is considerably smaller (162 meters in diameter, 5½ meters deep, measured from the rim), it is quite similar to the Arizona crater. Here also, meteoritic iron was found outside the crater, as well as large amounts of iron shale. A second smaller crater, 23 meters in diameter and 7 meters deep, is located near the main crater. Several thousand iron meteorite fragments were

---

*Maars are large craters formed by one or more explosive volcanic outbursts.

†Dolines, or sinks, are collapsed structures formed by water leaching away limestone or other rock at some depth. Limestone caverns, such as Mammoth Cave, Ky., represent another phase of the process that produces sinks.

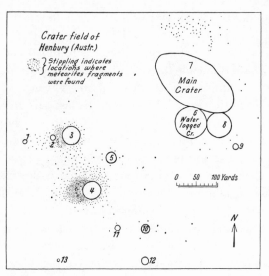

Crater field of
Henbury (Austr.)

Stippling indicates
locations where
meteorites fragments
were found

7
Main
Crater

6
Water
logged
Cr.

8

9

3

2

1

5

4

0 50 100 Yards

N

11

10

13

12

Fig. 20.—Crater field of Henbury, Australia. (After Alderman, in *Mineralogical Magazine*, 1932.)

found inside this crater. Geophysical and mining explorations begun in 1939 have again failed to discover the projectile.

The iron meteorites of both North American meteorite craters are so similar in structure and chemical composition that it is not improbable that both these craters were formed by a single shower of giant meteorites.

Further discoveries now followed in rapid succession. In 1930, R. A. Alderman found a field of no less than thirteen craters in Henbury, Central Australia (No. 3 on the map). Figure 20 shows the size, shape, and distribution of these craters. The largest (No. 7 "Main Crater") has an oval outline with diameters of 198 and

Fig. 21.—Interior view of the main crater of Henbury. (After Alderman.)

Fig. 22.—Jagged piece of meteorite iron from Henbury. Scale one-half natural size.

Fig. 23.—Partly fused sandstone from Henbury. About natural size.

108 meters, and its depth measured from the rim is 15 to 18 meters. An interior view is shown in Figure 21. At Henbury, too, many iron meteorites, totaling several hundred kilograms in weight, were found outside the craters, along with some iron shale. The locations at which many of these meteorites were found are indicated by points on the map (Fig. 20). Many of these irons, such as the one in Figure 22, have very peculiar shapes and look as if they were the shreds and tatters of larger pieces. The rock strata in the crater area consist of sandstone and shale. Here again, pieces of glassy or completely molten sandstone were found, such as the piece shown in Figure 23. During Alderman's second expedition—the crater-field is rather inaccessible—the smallest crater (No. 13), with a diameter of 9 meters, was excavated. At a depth of 2 meters iron meteorites cemented together by iron shale and weighing about 200 kilograms were found. These make up the last remains of the projectile that struck the crater. Excavations and shallow drillings in two of the other craters had no success.

Nothing certain is known about the age of these craters. It is again significant that the Australian aborigines do not camp in the vicinity. They call them "chindu chinna waru chingi yabu"

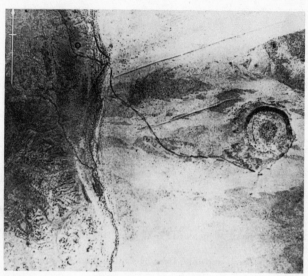

FIG. 24.—Meteorite crater of Wolf Creek, West Australia, aerial view. (After Guppy and Mathesun, in *Journal of Geology*, 1950.)

which means approximately sun-trail-fire-devil-stone. Here too this giant meteorite seems to have fallen as late as the age of man.*

Three additional meteorite craters have since been discovered in Australia. The first is also located in Central Australia, near Boxhole Station in the Plenty River area, McDonnell range (No. 4 on the map). Its diameter is about 175 meters, and its depth about 16 meters. Meteoritic iron and iron shale were found in its vicinity.

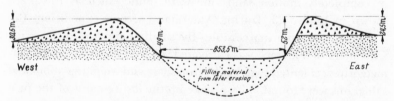

FIG. 25.—Cross-section of Wolf Creek meteorite crater. (After Guppy and Mathesun.)

---

*[Carbon-14 measurements by Goel and Kohman also indicate that the Henbury craters must have originated within the last few thousand years.—Translator]

The second largest of the definitely identified meteorite craters was discovered in 1947 by Reeves and Sauvé during a reconnaisance flight—the airplane plays an important role in the discovery of new meteorite craters. This crater is located at Wolf Creek in the Kimberley District, West Australia, south of Halls Creek (No. 6 on the map). Figure 24 shows an aerial view, and Figure 25 a cross-section of the crater. Meteoritic iron (though badly oxidized) and "iron shale" were found, but neither fused nor sintered rock material, although the area in which the crater is located is covered with sand and the underlying rock consists of Precambrian quartzites. The slight degree of weathering indicates a relatively low age.

The fourth Australian meteorite crater is also located in West Australia, at the sheep station Dalgaranga, near Yalgoo (No. 5 on the map). It has been known since 1910, but was not identified as a meteorite crater until 1938. Nickel-iron, badly weathered, has been found. The crater is the smallest of the four Australian ones. It has a diameter of only 68.5 meters and a depth of 4.5 meters. The meteoritic nature of a crater field near Mount Doreen, northwest of Alice Springs, North Territory, is still in doubt.

The iron meteorites of Henbury and Boxhole resemble each other so strongly in their structure and chemical composition that they probably belong to the same fall. It is not improbable that this is true of all four craters. In that case Australia must have been struck by a shower of giant meteorites. (But see note on Dalgaranga.)

A craterfield similar to that of Henbury was discovered in 1932 by the Englishman Philby near Wabar in the Rub al Khali desert in southern Arabia (No. 7 on the map). The purpose of Philby's expedition was to find the ruins of the legendary city Ad ibn Kin. This city plays an important role in the legends of the Arabs and is supposed to have been destroyed by fire from the sky, like Sodom and Gomorrah, because of the impiety of its king. Instead of the city, Philby found several crater-like formations, whose strange appearance in the middle of the sandy waste presumably gave rise to those legends. Figure 26 shows a map and Figure 27 a view of one of the craters. At the time of his visit, two craters (*A* and *B* in

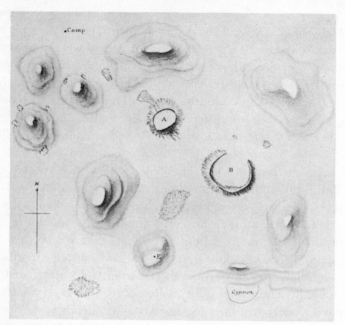

Fig. 26.—Crater field of Wabar, Arabia. (After Philby, in *Geographical Journal*, 1933.)

Fig. 26) could be seen. Two others (*C* and *D*) were buried under the desert sand. Presumably still other craters are hidden under the sand.

The craters of Wabar are noted for the plentiful occurrence of silica glass. Part of it is pumice- or slag-like, similar to the Henbury silica glass of Figure 23. Another part of it occurs as rounded bombs with a pumice-like core and an outer layer of bubble-free black silica glass, containing iron and nickel. In addition, black

Fig. 27.—View of one of the Wabar craters. (After Philby.)

glass beads are found in large quantities. In the vicinity of the craters, an iron meteorite and a small amount of iron shale were found. The diameter of the largest crater is about 100 meters, its depth about 10.5 meters. Philby's Arab guides could not be persuaded that the black beadlike objects were of a natural origin. They were sure that these "pearls" had belonged to the harem women of the legendary king killed by the heavenly fire, and they therefore stuffed their saddlebags with them to the bursting point. Later at the market in Mecca, they finally were forced to understand, to their dismay, that these were not genuine pearls.

In 1937, the meteoritic origin of the crater-field of the Sall Estate of Oesel Island in the gulf of Riga (No. 8 on the map) was fully proven by the discovery of meteoritic iron by I. A. Reinwald. These craters had been known for a long time and their origin had been debated at considerable length. Figure 28 shows the distribution of the craters. The main crater lies near the Sall Estate and reaches a depth of 14 to 16 meters (from the rim) and a maximum diameter of 110 meters. It has become filled by a small crater lake. Figure

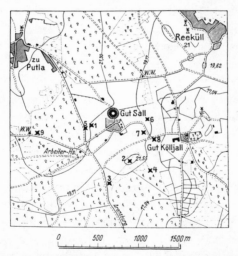

FIG. 28.—Crater field of Oesel. The smaller craters are indicated by crosses and numbered 1 through 9. (After Krauss, Meyer and Wegener, in *Gerl. Beitr. z. Geophys.,* 1928.)

29 shows an aerial view. These formations are younger than the last glaciation, which deposited the local subsoil.

FIG. 29.—Main crater of Oesel, aerial view. (After Reinwald, in *Natur und Volk,* 1940.)

While the meteoritic nature of craters 1 to 8 of Figure 14 has been established beyond doubt, the evidence is not yet conclusive for the remaining structures. In most of them, no trace of meteoritic material has been found. Others have not yet been studied in detail. But for some at least a meteoritic origin seems rather likely.

The largest of these structures and, if its meteoritic nature is confirmed, the largest of all meteorite craters, is the crater discovered in 1950 in the northwestern part of Québec Province in Canada (No. 9 on the map). It was the fourth crater to be discovered by means of aerial photography. This crater was spotted by the prospector, Chubb, after whom it has been named, on a Canadian Air Force aerial photograph (Fig. 30). Chubb believed it to be an explosion crater similar to the diamond-bearing pipes in South Africa. However, Victor B. Meen, Director of the Royal Ontario Museum, Toronto, believed it to be a meteorite crater. With some difficulty an aerial expedition was organized and a preliminary study made. The crater is situated in an extremely inhospitable region and is sunk into granitic rock and filled with water. The

FIG. 30.—Aerial view of the New Quebec crater in Canada. (From *Sky and Telescope,* 1951.)

crater wall (Fig. 31), consists of crumpled granite and is covered, as is the surrounding area, with granite boulders and a few blocks of dolerite and peridotite. The diameter of this perfectly circular crater is about 3,600 meters. The maximum height of the wall, measured from the surface of the lake, is about 180 meters. Neither

FIG. 31.—Interior view of New Quebec crater. (From *Scientific American,* 1951.)

volcanic nor meteoritic matter has been found so far. More detailed investigations later established the exact morphology of this structure, but still did not bring to light any meteoritic material.

A second circular crater was discovered in Canada by aerial photography. It lies in northern Labrador, about 700 kilometers ESE. of the Chubb crater, between Hebron and Chimo, and is filled with greenish water (No. 15 on the map). Meen assumes it to be also of meteoritic origin. Two more circular structures were found in the province of Ontario from aerial photographs taken near Brent (Algonquin Park) and near Holleford. These two are regarded as fossil meteorite craters, since they are filled with Paleozoic sediments. The Deep Bay of Reindeer Lake, Saskatchewan, is also believed to be a meteorite crater. No meteoritic material has been found associated with any of these craters so far. In northeastern Greenland, a Danish expedition discovered a crater-field from the air, for which a meteoritic origin has been assumed. Another crater-like structure, possibility of meteoritic origin, was reported on Amak Island (No. 10 on the map), north of the Alaskan Peninsula. This crater has a diameter of about 63 meters. The depth (from the crest of the rim) is 15 meters. A crater field in Campo del Cielo, Gran Chaco, Argentina (No. 11 on the map) is also believed to be meteoritic since large masses of meteoritic iron and shale have been found in its vicinity. The largest crater is oval, 78 × 65 meters. A smaller one, of 56 meters diameter, has a depth of only 5 meters from the crest of the rim.

Another crater discovered from the air was found in the western Sahara in 1938 near Hofrat Aouelloul, 40 kilometers southwest of Chinguetti (No. 12 on the map). Later (1950), it was visited by the French scientist Monod, who found large amounts of glass in and around the crater. This glass is much like the glass of the meteorite crater Wabar and the "Darwin glass" of Tasmania (see Appendix,

Fig. 32.—The crater of Aouelloul. (After Monod and Purquie, in *Bull. Inst. franç. Afrique noire.*)

Fig. 33.—Aerial view of crater of Talemzane, Sahara. (After R. Karpoff, *Meteoritics*, 1953.)

"Tektites"). The meteoritic nature of this crater thus becomes highly probable. Meteoritic iron, however, has not been found in it. Its form (Fig. 32) already shows quite heavy erosion. The local tribesmen have used it as a refuge in times of danger. Many neolithic tools are strewn about the crater, and on its rim two pre-Islamic graves have been found. Another very similar crater was found in the Sahara, 400 kilometers SSE of Algiers, a few kilometers from the watering place Talemzane (No. 13 on the map). It is about 1,750 meters across. The highest point of the crater rim lies 67 meters above the crater floor (Fig. 33). Meteoritic material was not found but here, too, neolithic tools and pre-Islamic graves were discovered.

Finally, we should mention some further leads: a crater that was discovered in an aerial photograph of the airlane between Cairo and Basra, but closer to Basra (No. 14 on the map), in an area that shows no volcanic activity of any kind. Nothing further is known about it. Two similar craters were spotted from an airplane in the neighborhood of Baghdad. The meteoritic nature of two craters of 45 to 80 meters, and 60 meters in diameter close to Murgab near Lake Saresk, Tadjikistan, U.S.S.R. is similarly unconfirmed.

Having covered this long list of relics of prehistoric catastrophes, we shall at last describe in detail an event that undoubtedly represents the fall of a giant meteorite. In this case, the point of impact

45

is known, but no structure that resembles a meteorite crater and no meteoritic material of any kind have yet been found. This event, which fortunately occurred in a very remote region of the Siberian taiga near the Stony Tunguska (a tributary of the Yenisei River), is full of mysteries, and it is high time that everything possible be done to examine closely the remaining traces, since in the fifty years that have passed they have become increasingly obscured by a new cover of vegetation.

A large number of eyewitness reports have established beyond any doubt that a gigantic meteorite fell in that area. On the morning of June 30, 1908, at about 6 A.M., passengers on the Trans-Siberian Railroad in Kansk saw a meteor as big and bright as the sun traverse the sky from south to north. After its disappearance beyond the northern horizon, they heard a thunderclap, and then several more. The thunder was so loud that the engineer put on the brakes, believing that an explosion had occurred on the train. Although the newspapers and magazines of the area published a large number of reports about this event, Russian scientists, strangely and regrettably, did not concern themselves with the matter. Yet the impact of the meteorite was so violent that it was recorded by sensitive seismographs at great distances. The seismographic stations of Irkutsk, Tashkent, Tiflis, and Jena reported an earth tremor, and the records of automatic barographs in southern England and Potsdam showed an air pressure wave traceable to the impact. Luminous clouds could be seen in the sky for several nights after the fall. From all these reports and instrumental records, it was established that the giant meteorite fell on June 30, 1908, at 0 hr. 10 min. 07 seconds (Greenwich time), near Chushmo River (Fig. 34), a small tributary of the Stony Tunguska, 65 kilometers NNE. of the Vanovara factory at the Stony Tunguska (60° 65' north, 101° 57' east, No. 16 on the map).

What was recorded in Europe only by sensitive instruments was observed closer to the impact point as a violent shock wave. In the Vanovara factory, windows were smashed and doors lifted from their hinges. The yurts (portable huts) of the Tungus nomads were knocked down, and, though there was no human loss of life, their

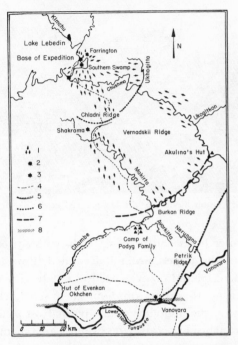

FIG. 34.—Fall area of the Tunguska meteorite. (1) razed forest, (2) point of fall, (3) astronomically surveyed point, (4) trails, (5) road to the factory, Strelka, (6) limit of fire, (7) limit of broken-down forest, (8) limit of explosion shock wave. Scale about 1:1,000,000. (After E. Krinov, *The Tunguska Meteorite.*)

reindeer stampeded, and more than a thousand are supposed to have been killed. Not until 1927 did Kulik, the Russian meteoriticist, succeed, through his zeal and scientific enthusiasm, in raising the funds for an expedition to the presumed impact point. He found the spot that is today thought to be the place of fall. Later expeditions followed. In one of these, Kulik, who was killed in World War II, was accompanied by the Russian meteoriticist Krinov, who eventually collected all the observational material in the book *The Tunguska Meteorite* (in Russian, 1949).

During the 1927 expedition, Kulik found in a swampy area a number of open water holes of 10 to 32 meters diameter (Fig. 35). In spite of their quite uncharacteristic form he at first thought them to be meteorite craters. But Krinov could show convincingly

Fig. 35.—The "crater field" in the Taiga. (After Kulik, in *Geographical Journal*, 1933.)

that these water holes had nothing to do with meteorite craters. Excavation of the largest water hole and drilling furnished no meteoritic material and no evidence for a meteoritic origin of the holes. According to expert opinion, such structures quite frequently occur at the boundary of the permafrost zone. Kulik had come to his conclusion because the swampy area mentioned above was located at the center of an approximately circular area of destruction (See Fig. 34). Directly adjoining the swampy area is

Fig. 36.—Razed forest. (After Kulik, from Nininger, *Our Stone-pelted Planet* [Boston and New York, 1935].)

48

the "fire zone." Here were clear signs that the original forest had been burned off. The fire zone extends about 20 kilometers southeastward from the central swamp. Further outward is the "zone of the felled forest," where the trees were snapped off like reeds. Observations from the ground and air show that the trunks lie radially outward from the central swamp (Figs. 34 and 36). This zone extends up to about 40 kilometers southeastward. In one part of the forest, only the treetops were snapped off. This area (Fig. 37) looks like a forest of telegraph poles. Still further out, the forest gradually resumes its normal appearance. The destructive pressure wave extended to the area of the Vanovara factory, about 65 kilometers from the impact center. Up to this distance, trees with broken-off tops were found occasionally.

In 1953, the impact point was visited once more, this time by an aerial expedition of the Meteorite Committee of the Academy of Sciences in Moscow. The site was still recognizable from the air. Two completely circular lakes about 100 meters across were observed about 15–20 kilometers southwest of Lake Cheko (about 6 kilometers northwest of the impact center). Further investigation will show whether the real meteorite craters have at last been discovered.

The upshot of all these observations is that an enormous explosion clearly did occur in this area, and that it is connected, accord-

Fig. 37.—"Telegraph pole" forest. (After Kulik, *Atlantis,* 1929.)

ing to the testimony of the inhabitants, with the fall of the meteorite. The actual impact point of the projectile has not yet been found. Also, no meteoritic material of any kind has been detected. It is possible that this giant meteorite, unlike all other giant meteorites that have fallen on the earth, would be difficult to identify after such a long time without a careful and extensive search. Possibly some clues could be obtained by systematic soil sampling in the presumed impact area.* The apparent lack of a crater has caused Lincoln LaPaz, a meteoriticist at the University of New Mexico, to propose that the Tunguska Meteorite consisted of "anti-matter," that is, matter in which the atomic nucleus consists of negatively charged particles (anti-protons) and an electronic shell of positively charged elementary particles (positrons). Upon collision of this anti-matter with terrestrial matter, even matter as tenuous as the upper atmosphere, it is annihilated, being converted to radiation, so that no meteoritic material survives. The evidence available up to now does not seem to justify such an unorthodox explanation.

Concluding this discussion of meteorite craters, we shall add a list of craters or crater-like formations alleged to be of meteoritic origin. It is certain, however, that these are not meteorite craters.†

Europe	Nördlinger Ries; Steinheim Basin, Köfels Hollows in the Ötz Valley; the Hungarian Plain (!).
Asia	Gwarkuk, Baluchistan; Lake Lonar, India.
Africa	Lake Bosumtwi, Ashanti, Ghana; Salt Pan, Pretoria.
America	Carolina Bays; Tiffin, Iowa.

If we now review the evidence placed before us, two remarkable facts stand out. First, all eight verified craters were made by gigantic iron meteorites. It has not been shown with certainty that this preponderance of the irons over the stones is caused by a faster

---

*[In 1958, A Yavnel reported the discovery of small metallic spherules in the soil near the presumed impact area. By analogy with other meteorite craters, these spherules may well be meteorite material that had vaporized on impact with the earth.—Translator]

†[At least three of these structures, the Nördlinger Ries, the Steinheim Basin, and Lake Bosumtwi are now presumed to be meteoritic, as suggested by the discovery of coesite at these localities.—Translator]

rate of weathering of stone meteorites and the inconspicuousness of their fragments. Further information is necessary in order to decide whether this circumstance is of any importance. The second fact can be stated in the form of a question. Where are the giant meteorites that have punched out these gigantic holes and of which, as we saw, only minute traces, or none at all, have been found? The stated observations and a brief calculation lead to the conclusion *that they have been almost completely destroyed during impact with the earth*, that they exploded and were vaporized to a gas cloud. In an earlier section, discussing the velocity of meteorites striking the ground, it has been pointed out that low terminal velocities apply only to meteorites in the size range commonly found on earth, that is, not more than a few tons in weight. When the masses become appreciably larger, conditions change drastically.

Let us return to Tables 3 and 4 on page 22, for we have not yet discussed the figures in the last four columns. They show us that from a certain mass of the meteorite on, our atmosphere no longer suffices to brake the cosmic velocity of the meteorite. As these tables and Figure 38 make clear, the "point of retardation" mentioned above moves farther and farther down into the atmosphere with increasing mass of the meteorite and finally reaches the earth's surface itself. In other words, these giant meteorites strike the earth's surface with a substantial fraction of their cosmic velocity unimpaired. How much this raises the impact velocity will be shown in an example, Figure 38. Let us consider a series of meteorites ranging in weight from $\frac{1}{10}$ to 1,000 tons, falling vertically ($i = 90°$) and with an entry velocity of 40 kilometers per second. These curves show that masses of one-tenth of a ton to one ton are braked at heights of 16 and 8 kilometers. A meteorite of ten tons will just barely be brought to terminal velocity by the atmosphere if it enters at 40 kilometers per second, whereas one of 100 tons will hit the ground at nearly 20 kilometers per second, and one of 1,000 tons at almost 29 kilometers per second. Remembering the above-mentioned formula for the kinetic energy, $E = \frac{1}{2} mv^2$, we see that these enormous increases in mass and velocity

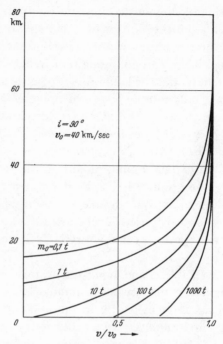

FIG. 38.—Deceleration of meteorites of different mass.

bring about a corresponding increase of the energy content. If the mass is expressed in grams and the velocity in centimeters per second, the energy, E, is obtained in ergs, the unit of work. The erg is a very small unit; it corresponds approximately to the work required to raise a one-milligram weight one centimeter. (The meter kilogram is somewhat better known; it is the work required to raise one kilogram one meter. One mkg $= 9.81 \times 10^7$ ergs.) Hence, according to Table 4, an iron meteorite of 100 tons has an energy content of 1.75×10^{12} ergs per gram, and one of 1,000 tons, 4.06×10^{12} ergs per gram. The energy of the impacting meteorite is spent in digging the crater, producing the earthquake and air waves, heating the rocks at the impact point (recall the fused sandstone pieces from the meteorite craters), and finally in heating the meteorite itself. Let us see what fraction of the total energy is required for the latter purpose. First, we calculate just how many ergs are required to heat one gram of iron, initially at very low temperature, to the boiling point of iron (approximately 3,200°C) —about 7.9×10^{10} ergs per gram, or not quite 10^{11} ergs per gram. Iron meteorites of 100 tons and above, with an energy content of 10^{12} ergs per gram under the conditions stated, can easily furnish these 10^{11} ergs for the vaporization of the meteorite, and still retain more than 90 per cent of their energy for other impact effects. This result, which is not significantly different at other entry velocities, is in agreement with experience to date. No meteoritic irons of 100 tons or greater mass are known. They would be objects of very conspicuous appearance, and it is not likely that they should have escaped our attention thus far. On the other hand, the dimensions of meteorite craters are so large that projectiles with mass far greater than 1,000 tons must be assumed. Hence, there is no longer any point in looking for these giant meteorites. Only small traces, if anything, will be found. This second consequence of our calculation has been confirmed by experience thus far without exception.

NUMBER OF FALLS

Now that we have learned something about meteorite falls, we naturally want to know on how many occasions material has been recovered. Up to now, material from about 683 observed falls has been secured, but this does not exhaust the total amount at our disposal. To these 683 falls some 865 "finds" should be added (a "find" is a meteorite whose descent has not been observed) so that altogether about 1,548 meteorites are known. Every year several new falls and finds are added. Table 8 shows the frequency of the principal types of meteorites. This list includes the 1,548 meteorites described in the catalogue of Prior and Hey; the statistics include material up to about 1953.

We are already familiar with the difference between stone and iron meteorites. The other terms in this table are discussed in the chapter on the classification of meteorites, p. 116.

This table is of interest in several respects; first of all, the stone meteorites are by far the most numerous and among them the so-

TABLE 8

	Falls	Finds	Total
All meteorites	683	865	1,548
All Stones	638	317	955
Achondrites	57	11	68
Chondrites	523	254	777
Siderolites	9	11	20
Unclassified	49	41	90
All Irons	45	548	593
Lithosiderites	3	44	47
Hexahedrites	6	36	42
Octahedrites	29	376	405
Ataxites	1	56	57
Unclassified	6	36	42

called chondrites are the most common. Among the iron meteorites, too, a certain type, the octahedrites, are particularly common. At first glance, the ratio of observed falls to finds seems unusual. For all types combined, this ratio is about 1 to 1. However, observed falls comprise 80.6 per cent of the stones but only 6.5 per cent of the irons. The reason for this striking difference is that the stone meteorites, because of their great resemblance to certain terrestrial rocks, and because of their greater tendency to weather, escape detection much more easily if they are not recovered soon after the fall. The blocks of nickel-rich iron, on the other hand, resist weathering, generally speaking, and are so conspicuous when on the ground that they can easily be recognized as meteorites even if no record of their fall exists.

DISTRIBUTION OF FALLS IN TIME AND SPACE

Do meteorites fall in some regions of the earth more frequently than in others? If we analyze the available data statistically, we obtain the results shown in Table 9. Of the 1,388 meteorites known before 1940, Europe accounts for 335; Asia, 226; Africa, 71; America, 662, and Australia, 91. But closer scrutiny of these so strikingly disproportionate numbers shows, as previously pointed out by the Viennese meteoriticist Berwerth (using much more limited data), that these differences in distribution are not caused by a preference of meteorites for some continents. Instead, this distribution is governed by the density and cultural level of the population. For example, of the 71 African meteorites, no less than 34 were either found or seen to fall in South Africa. Of the 226 Asian ones, 111 come from the densely populated Indian subcontinent. And of the 662 American ones, only 80 come from South America compared to 499 in the United States.

But this explanation cannot account for another peculiarity. For example, from the Western Hemisphere, 358 irons against only 304 stones have been reported, but from the Eastern Hemisphere, including Eurasia and Africa, 115 irons and 517 stones. It has been suggested that in the Old World, with its long history of agriculture, the iron meteorites had already been picked up during cultivation of the soil in primitive times and were then worked into tools or weapons, whereas in the desert-like regions of the New World they have been preserved to the present day. (See also the chapter "Historical Facts Concerning Meteorites" p. 61.)

The 1,400 known meteorites mentioned above were nearly all found within the last 150 years. In the years before 1790, only about twenty falls were described. Nor is the number of finds from that period large. According to a study by Mason, the 670 observed falls from the period 1800–1960 for which detailed information is available are distributed according to the curve in Figure 39. Here the meteorite falls of each decade are grouped together, and it is seen that the number of observed falls has risen from about one per year in the decade 1800–09 to about eight per year in the decade 1930–39. This is not due to an increase in the frequency of fall in these 130 years; rather, higher population density, improved communications, and greater interest on the part of the general public have brought more meteorite falls to the attention of science than in previous years. However, the strikingly high figures for the years 1868 (11) and 1933 (15) are not yet completely understood.

These 591 meteorites are far from representing the total amount of meteorite material that has fallen on the earth in 150 years. We have only to remember that about 72 per cent of the earth's surface is covered with water and that large land areas are either completely uninhabited or only very sparsely populated. By far the greater part of the meteorites striking the earth thus escape discovery and investigation. Latest estimates by Brown (California Institute of Technology) assume a yearly total of about 500 meteorites for the entire earth, of which on the average only about seven become available for scientific investigation! This shows how

TABLE 9

	Stones	Irons	Total
Austria	4	0	4
Belgium	3	0	3
Czechoslovakia	14	9	23
Denmark	1	0	1
England	12	1	13
Finland	6	1	7
France	55	1	56
Germany	25	11	36
Hungary	5	1	6
Ireland	5	1	6
Italy	17	1	18
Netherlands	3	0	3
Norway	6	2	8
Poland	3	0	3
Portugal	4	0	4
Rumania	7	0	7
Spain	25	4	29
Sweden	7	1	8
Switzerland	5	1	6
U.S.S.R. (European part)	68	10	78
Yugoslavia	6	1	7
Remaining Balkan countries and Turkey	8	1	9
Europe Total	289	46	335

	Stones	Irons	Total
Arabia	4	3	7
China	5	0	5
India and Pakistan	106	5	111
Japan	25	9	34
Java	6	2	8
Philippines	3	0	3
U.S.S.R. (Asiatic part)	21	21	42
Rest of Asia	15	1	16
Asia Total	185	41	226

	Stones	Irons	Total
Algeria	4	3	7
Former French West Africa	4	3	7
South-West Africa	1	3	4
Union of South Africa	19	15	34
Rest of Africa	15	4	19
Africa Total	43	28	71

	Stones	Irons	Total
Australia with Tasmania and New Zealand	33	58	91
Canada with Greenland	6	14	20
Mexico	10	45	55
U.S.A. without Alaska	253	246	499
Rest of North America	2	3	5
North America Total	271	308	579
Central America Total	1	2	3

	Stones	Irons	Total
Argentina	12	3	15
Bolivia	0	3	3
Brazil	9	7	16
Chile	9	34	43
Rest of South America	2	1	3
South America Total	32	48	80
America Total	304	358	662
Others	3	0	3
Grand Total for entire Earth	857	531	1,388

careful one must be in the interpretation of statistical results.

Are there any seasonal trends in the fall of meteorites? This question is important because its answer might provide a clue to the relations between meteorites and comets or known meteor showers. The curve in Figure 40 gives an answer. It includes 670

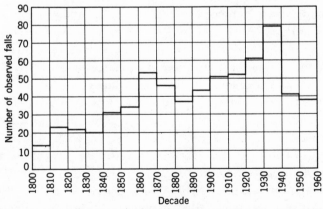

Fig. 39.—Recovery of observed meteorite falls by decades, 1800–1960. (Reprinted with permission from Brian Mason, *Meteorites* [New York, 1962].)

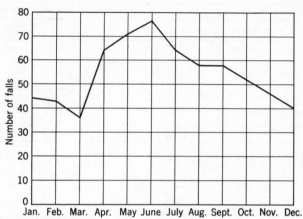

Fig. 40.—Monthly variation in the incidence of meteorite falls, 1800–1960. (Reprinted with permission from Brian Mason, *Meteorites*.)

falls from the previously mentioned statistics and shows an absolute maximum in the month of June. The values for May and April are also quite high. The absolute minimum occurs in March and the values for the winter months are quite low. This maximum must be partially caused by the fact that most observations come from the northern hemisphere where, of course, the summer months are more suitable for the observation of meteorites than the winter months. But according to this argument there should be hardly any difference between September and October, on the one hand, and April and May on the other. Thus it seems that during the months of the maximum the earth crosses a region in space that contains a higher density of meteorites. No obvious relations to known meteor showers or comets are found. In fact, meteors have a minimum in May and June and a maximum in July and September. Let us make a note of this finding for later reference.

The distribution of meteorite falls versus the days of the month shows nothing striking. In contrast, a plot of the *hours* of fall shows a pronounced maximum. Of 469 meteorites whose time of fall is well known, 187 have fallen between midnight and noon, and 282 between noon and midnight, as shown in Figure 41. The maxi-

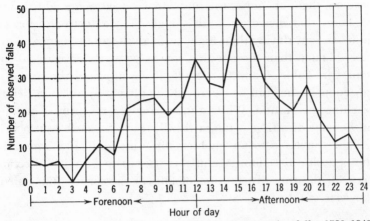

FIG. 41.—Hourly variation in the incidence of meteorite falls, 1790–1940. (Leonard and Slanin, 1941.) (Reprinted with permission from Brian Mason, *Meteorites.*)

mum lies at 3:00 P.M., the second peak at 12:00 noon, and the minimum at 3:00 A.M. These times of fall are significant because they provide information on the direction of the meteorites' arrival. All those that fall from noon to midnight have the same direction of motion as the earth, while those falling from midnight to noon either collide with the earth head-on or are overtaken by it. This can be seen plainly in Figure 42. Obviously the time of fall is related to the velocity with which the meteorite enters the earth's atmosphere. If both the meteorite and the earth move in the same direction, the entry velocity is the difference between the orbital velocity of the earth (29.77 kilometers per second on the average) and that of the meteorite. If, on the other hand, the meteorite moves in the opposite direction and strikes the earth

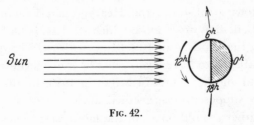

FIG. 42.

59

head-on, then, of course, the individual velocities are added. But we know that meteorites with a high entry velocity are heated more strongly during their flight through the atmosphere and are more ablated than those with a low velocity. Refer again to the figures in Tables 5 and 6, page 25, for example. If their mass is low enough, they can be destroyed completely by ablation before reaching the ground. While a meteorite of a given mass moving in the same direction as the earth will reach the earth's surface, it will be converted to an unobservable dust grain if it moves in the opposite direction. Again, there seems to be no connection between the time-distribution of falls of meteorites and meteor showers.

THE HAZARDS OF FALLS

And now to a practical aspect of meteorite falls that concerns us directly. We have seen, to be sure, that the impact effects of ordinary meteorites are not very impressive, in spite of the thunder and lightning accompanying their fall. Nevertheless, if one considers that most meteorites weigh more than a kilogram, and that occasionally as many as 100,000 stones come thundering down, one can imagine that it is not particularly pleasant to find oneself at the time and place of their fall. But history and statistics provide some encouragement. Thus far, not a single well-confirmed case is known in which a man has been killed by a meteorite. True, it occurs in many stories—for example, the description in the Bible, Josh. 10:11, of the struggle between the Israelites and the Amorites is regarded by some as an example of a meteorite shower with deadly consequences: "And it came to pass, as they fled from before Israel, and were in the going down to Beth-Horon, that the Lord cast down great stones from Heaven upon them unto Azekah, and they died: they were more which died with hailstones than they whom the children of Israel slew with the sword." Further, a monk is alleged to have been killed by a meteorite in Cremona in 1511, and another monk in Milan in 1650. In 1674, two Swedish sailors supposedly were killed aboard their ship. Of these reports, neither the old ones nor the more recent ones have with-

60

stood critical investigation. For example, some years ago a wedding guest is supposed to have been killed in one of the Balkan countries, and then a child in Japan, and finally, in 1906 the rebel general, T. Catillianis, in a military camp. Perhaps the greatest danger was faced by three children in Braunau in Bohemia. In 1847, a 17-kilogram iron meteorite fell into the room in which they were sleeping, covering them with debris from the ceiling, but fortunately none of them was seriously hurt. A century later, on November 30, 1954, a woman was slightly injured in Sylacauga, Alabama, by a stone meteorite weighing 3.855 kilograms. This meteorite struck her after penetrating the roof and ceiling of her house.

In principle, it is of course possible for a man to be struck by a meteorite, but the probability is quite small. We must always consider how minute a fraction of the earth's surface is covered by human bodies. It has been calculated, for example, that in the United States, on the average, a man will be struck by a meteorite once in every 9,300 years—a comforting thought! Nevertheless, it is remarkable that not even large showers, some of which have fallen in densely populated regions, have ever injured people. Another calculation by American scientists has indicated that only one out of sixty-six meteorites is likely to hit a village or a town.

We have only a few reports of animals killed by meteorites. For example, in 1911 a dog was killed by the meteorite of Nakhla (in Egypt), and in 1860, a colt, by a stone of the meteorite shower of New Concord, Ohio. But buildings have been damaged in many instances, for example, by the meteorites of Ausson (France, 1851), Barbotan (France, 1790); Benares (India, 1798); Braunau (Bohemia, 1847); Mässing (Bavaria, 1803); and Pillistfer (Estonia, 1863). Altogether about twelve cases of damage to buildings are known.

HISTORICAL FACTS CONCERNING METEORITES

If the striking effects of meteorite falls evoke fear and panic in modern man, they did so even more in times past when people's views of nature and the constitution of the heavens were governed by religion and myth. Those brightly glowing stars, that seemed

61

to have suddenly fallen from the firmament, aroused great interest. This interest increased when some of these falling stars were found and collected, and the story of the recognition of the true nature of meteorites is most fascinating. In particular, it is a warning to the natural scientist, reminding him to approach the explanation of strange phenomena with a critical, but unprejudiced mind.

The scientific study of meteorites is only about 150 years old, but the knowledge of these objects reaches much farther back into the past. Long before man learned to smelt iron from its ores, he seems to have used meteoritic iron to produce artifacts of various kinds, as was the case until recently with the Eskimo and several Negro tribes. Comparative linguistics tells us that "iron" is related in many languages to the words "sky" and "star." For instance, the Greek word for iron is sideros and the Latin word for star, sidera. In ancient Egyptian, the word for iron meant "metal from heaven." In an inventory of a Hittite king's treasury, iron is listed as "iron from heaven" along with gold and silver from various mines. Other peoples, such as the Australian aborigines and the American Indians, did not know what to do with these gifts from heaven, although they occur rather frequently in the countries they lived in. The peculiar distribution of meteoritic irons and stones mentioned on p. 54 seems to be related to the early utilization of meteoritic iron by the ancients and their esteem for it. On Oesel Island, with its long history of human occupation, only a few sparse remains of the iron meteorite shower that fell in prehistoric times have been found after intensive searches and digs. In contrast, many tons of meteoritic iron are strewn about in South West Africa, South America, Mexico, and Australia and have not been exploited to an appreciable degree.

The meteorites of the Anderson and Hopewell mounds in Ohio are regarded as prehistoric. Peoples with a long cultural history, such as the Chinese, Egyptians, Greeks, and Romans showed a keen interest in meteorites and have left many records about meteorite falls as well as finds. In the great Chinese encyclopedia, Mu Tuan Lin (1245–1325) reports falls spanning about two millenia. Anaxagoras, Plutarch, Livy, Pliny, and many other ancient writers report meteorite falls in their writings. Only a few examples will be given. About 625 B.C. a shower of stones fell in the Alban Mountains near Rome; in 465 B.C. a stone fell in Thrace near the River Aegos (Aegos-Potamos). In 204 B.C. a stone that had fallen in Phrygia somewhat earlier was brought to Rome with great ceremony.

Meteorites were regarded as fallen stars or as messengers of the gods and were therefore frequently the object of religious adoration. A "holy stone" in the temple of the goddess Diana in Ephesus and a relic in the temple of Venus in Cyprus are believed to have been meteorites. In Rome, during the reign of Numa Pompilius, a small shield-shaped iron meteorite was worshiped in the belief that its possession assured rule of the world. In order to prevent loss by theft, the shrewd Roman priests had eleven facsimile iron shields made. Occasionally, meteorite falls were also immortalized on coins. Figure 43 shows such a coin referring to the death of Caesar. The "Hadshar al Aswad," a black stone mounted in silver in the holy of holies in the Kaaba in Mecca, is believed to be a meteorite. The legend tells us it was originally white and became black through the sins of man. Some primitive tribes worship meteorites to this day.

Weapons of all kinds have been made from iron meteorites since ancient times. Sword blades from Arabia are known that were supposed to make their bearers invulnerable. The Mogul emperor, Jehangir, had a sword, dagger, and knife made from a meteorite in 1621; and even in recent times, the Sultan of Solo in Java had a number of kris (daggers) made from the iron of Prambanan (known

Fig. 43.—Meteorite coin

Vlon dem donnerstein gefallé im rcij. tar: vor Enfisheim

FIG. 44.—Fall of Ensisheim, Alsace, meteorite

since 1797), which he gave away as princely presents. Knives and nails were also made from iron meteorites, and larger blocks often served as anvils.

In the middle ages, meteorites, just as comets, were regarded as signs from God, but, in contrast to the ancient times, as a sign of his wrath. The oldest meteorite fall of which material has still been preserved is that of Ensisheim in Alsace. This stone meteorite fell on November 16, 1492 (New Style), at 11:30 A.M., after a violent detonation. Figure 44 shows a picture of the fall according to a contemporary broadside. Sebastian Brant (1457–1521) composed a Latin poem in commemoration of this event.

The main part of the stone, weighing 54.75 kilograms, is still kept in the town hall at Ensisheim. The Emperor Maximilian referred to this fall in a proclamation as a sign of God directed against the Turks. The stone fall of Osterau (1671) was also claimed to be "a sign of the Almighty's wrath and a warning of the Turk's stony heart and furious manner in which he sets himself against the precious Christian blood."

Contemporary scholars did not know what to do with the stone of Ensisheim. Finally, they declared this fall to be one of God's own miracles. In later times, particularly during the period of the Enlightenment, the scientific world rejected this belief in miracles, and since many of the reports of meteorite falls were wrong, fantastic, or exaggerated, they refused to believe any of them, thus

64

FIG. 45.—The Ensisheim meteorite

throwing out the baby with the bath water, and relegated even the well-confirmed case histories to the realm of old wives' tales and "absurdities." The French Academy especially stood out in this respect. One of its commissions, which included among its members the famous chemist Lavoisier (though only twenty-five years old at the time), declared the meteorite of Lucé (1768) to be a variety of pyrite. Concerning the stone meteorite shower of Barbotan (France, 1790), which was well confirmed by the mayor and the city council, the French scientist Bertholon wrote: "How sad it is to see a whole municipality attempt to lend credibility, through a formal deposition, to folk tales that arouse the pity not only of physicists but of all sensible people." In Germany, X. Stütz wrote, "Of course it is said that in both cases [meteorites of Agram, Croatia, 1761, and Eichstädt, Bavaria, 1785] the iron fell from the sky. Even the more enlightened minds in Germany may have believed that in 1751, in view of the terrible ignorance then prevailing of natural history and practical physics. But in our times it would be unforgiveable to regard such fairy tales as likely." In spite of this rejection, Stütz regarded both meteorites as being of sufficient interest to save them and others, thereby laying the foundations of the famous Vienna meteorite collection.*

The first man to have the courage to oppose the prevailing authoritarian views on the basis of unprejudiced investigations was the German, Chladni (1756–1827). He was a physicist who became well known through his researches in acoustics. On his numerous journeys, he collected, among other things, reports on meteorite falls. He summarized his own observations on meteorites, and those of others, in the little book: *On the Origin of the Iron Masses found by Pallas, and Others Similar to It, and on Some Natural Phenomena Related to Them,* published in 1794. He concluded that the meteorites were the relics of fireballs and must be of extra-terrestrial origin. His views ran into the strongest opposition and were often ridiculed. In fact, his contemporaries, though receptive to mysticism, went so far as to believe that he had merely intended to poke fun at those physicists who might be fools enough to believe him. His famous colleague Lichtenberg said about the book, that "reading it made him feel at first as if he himself had been hit on the head by one of these rocks." Others accused Chladni of belonging to those who "deny any world order, and do not realize how much they are to blame for all the evil in the moral world." However, nature came to Chladni's aid. In 1803 a large meteorite shower fell at L'Aigle (France). It was verified by irreproachable witnesses and thus had to be recognized by the Academy in Paris.

Nowadays it has become customary to condemn Chladni's contemporaries for their narrow-mindedness. This is perhaps not quite fair. None of these scientists had himself witnessed a meteorite fall. Neither had Chladni, and he was therefore unable to bring forward any new and irrefutable direct evidence of his own. Thus his fellow-scientists had to decide how far they could trust the avail-

---

*[No less a person than Thomas Jefferson displayed the same incredulity on hearing of the Weston, Conn., meteorite (December 26, 1807), which had been investigated by Professors Silliman and Kingsley of Yale. He remarked that it was easier to believe that Yankee professors would lie, than that stones would fall from heaven.—Translator]

able reports, coming as they did entirely from laymen. As we saw above, such lay reports are often fantastic, uncritical, or totally false. Every meteoriticist, even in our times, has a tale to tell about this. In those days, when the natural scientists had just begun to free themselves from the tutelage of tradition, the state, and established religion, these scientists were firmly resolved to recognize only what they were able to confirm by their own observations. They did not yet have the more than 150 years' experience available to their present-day successors. It was obviously quite difficult for them to sift a few correct reports from the majority of wrong ones. The problem of recognizing a genuine meteorite fall was no longer a scientific one, but a psychological one, requiring mainly the correct evaluation of eyewitness accounts. F. A. Paneth, a meteoriticist last active in Mainz (died 1958), first pointed out this circumstance and noted that Chladni had been a lawyer before he became a scientist. Thus Chladni was well-versed in a field that concerns itself a great deal with the evaluation of testimony.

After Chladni's views had won full recognition, active collection and investigation of meteorites began. Suddenly they had become objects of the greatest interest, and for a long time they were the only clues to the composition of extra-terrestrial bodies.

We shall discuss the nature of meteoritic matter in the next few chapters, now that we have learned the principal phenomena accompanying the encounter of these celestial bodies with our earth. But first, two sections of practical importance.

The fall of a meteorite occurs so rarely and so unexpectedly that experts cannot count on observing one, except by accident. We are therefore dependent on the help of the public in this respect. Owing to the suddenness of these events, the great majority of lay observers are taken completely by surprise, particularly since they usually witness only one such fall during their lifetimes. Thus it is understandable that the observations reported are frequently incomplete. Trivial phenomena are considered important and are recorded, whereas significant observational data are overlooked, forgotten, or determined with insufficient accuracy.

WHAT TO LOOK OUT FOR IN A METEORITE FALL

First a general rule: All observations, especially numerical ones, should be put down on paper without delay. It is hard to believe how unreliable one's memory can be! And now a few points that should be watched for in particular.

1. At what time (day, hour, minute) did the meteorite appear? As soon as possible, compare your watch with an accurate clock, or get a time signal from the radio, TV, or telephone.

2. How long did the light phenomenon last from the time it was first spotted to disappearance? Count the seconds (21 and . . . 22 and . . . 23 and . . . , etc.), since there is no time to look at your watch. This counting method is better than any other kind of estimate.

3. How bright and how large was the fireball? Compare with stars or moon.

4. What shape did the light phenomenon have—sparks, lightning-like flashes, explosive bursts, etc.? Sketch these on paper if possible.

5. What was the color of the light in the different parts of the path?

6. Was a luminous train, a smoke cloud, or some other trail observable?

7. How long did this trail remain in the sky? What was its appearance and color?

8. Where in the sky was the path of the fireball located? An accurate answer to this question is of particular interest. In clear weather, the orientation of the path can be located with respect to stars or constellations; in cloudy weather or during the day, it can be located relative to objects on the earth, that is, houses, church steeples, trees, mountains. The position of the observer is very important and should also be recorded. Estimates of position in degrees are reliable only if the observer has a great deal of experience. The end point of the path should be determined as accurately as possible.

9. How many minutes and seconds elapsed between the first appearance of the light and the arrival of the first sound?

10. What was the sound like? Did it resemble thunder, pops, a crash, a roll, a growl, or a hiss? How long did it last?

11. How much time went by between the fall and the first discovery of the meteorite?

12. Was the meteorite hot or cold? Any evidence of heat, smoke, or odor?

13. Did only one meteorite fall or were there several? Record weights and dimensions. If several fell, indicate their places of fall on a sketch, giving the weights. Inquire in the neighborhood, as the individual pieces are often found several miles distant from one another.

14. What was the soil like in the vicinity of the impact point? (Plowed field, forest, meadow, road, sand, moist, dry, frozen, etc.) Were any trees or buildings damaged?

15. How deeply did the meteorite penetrate the ground? If several pieces were found, give this information separately for each piece, identifying them by size and weight. Was the meteorite broken on impact?

16. What shape, size, inclination did the impact hole have?

17. Did the meteorite reach the ground before or after the sound phenomena?

Pictures should be taken from as many different angles as possible, always with a suitable scale (people, yardstick, watch, etc.)

HOW DOES ONE RECOGNIZE A METEORITE?

The experts need the help of the public in yet another respect. As we saw above, only about one-half of the 1,500 or so known meteorites were observed as they fell. This raises the question: What methods are available to science to recognize meteorites whose fall has not been observed? Have we not committed an error opposite to that of eighteenth-century scientists by assuming all too uncritically that all bodies of unusual composition found on earth have a meteoritic nature? A glance at Table 8 should reassure the reader. Except for the single class of nickel-rich ataxites, all the different varieties that were first classified as meteorites on the basis of finds alone were later confirmed by observed falls. If the criteria are not

FIG. 46.—Stone meteorite from Pultusk, Poland. About natural size.
FIG. 47.—Stone meteorite of Bath Furnace, Kentucky. (After Farrington.)

yet sufficient to establish a meteoritic origin to everyone's satisfaction, as is the case for tektites (see the chapter on these objects, p. 132), such objects are not now being thrown away, as some museum curators are said to have done in the past, for fear of ridicule, but are being collected and investigated most thoroughly. Some day we will understand their true nature.

There is no single criterion valid for each and every meteorite that would permit us to distinguish them from terrestrial rocks and artifacts. Only by a combination of several criteria can meteorites be characterized as a group.

Thin black fusion crusts, dull or lustrous, covering the object

FIG. 48.—Spinel with black, dull surface, similar to that of a meteorite. Natural size.
FIG. 49.—Stone meteorite of Farmington, Kansas, with iron grains. About natural size.

FIG. 50.—Basalt from Ovifak, Greenland, with iron grains. About natural size.

FIG. 51.—Stone meteorite of Bjurböle, Finland, with chondrules. (After Merrill, in *U.S. National Museum Bulletin 149*.)

completely, and shallow pits resembling thumb prints though they may be larger (see Figs. 46–47), point to a meteoritic origin. But there are meteorites without these identifying marks and, on the other hand, natural or artificial terrestrial materials showing similar surface features, for instance the spinel in Figure 48.

The presence of metallic iron grains in a stony matrix (Fig. 49) is suggestive of a meteoritic origin. But there are some meteorites without iron grains, and there are a few terrestrial rocks (Fig. 50) and artifacts that do contain them.

The presence of small, round globules, the so-called chondrules (see p. 114) is an important criterion for stone meteorites (Fig. 51),

FIG. 52.—Spherulitic greenstone of Schemnitz, with objects superficially resembling chondrules. (After Merrill.)

71

but again there are meteorites without such globules, and terrestrial rocks that contain superficially similar objects (Fig. 52).

For iron meteorites, the Widmanstätten pattern (see p. 105) that appears after brief etching with acid is characteristic (Figs. 53 *a, b*). Such damascened figures have never yet been found in native or artificial terrestrial iron. Nevertheless, metal objects lacking this pattern could still be genuine meteorites.

Characteristic of all iron meteorites is their nickel content, ranging from about 5 to 20 per cent, and a cobalt content about one-twentieth that value. Terrestrial native iron also contains nickel but either in small amounts (about 3 per cent) or in larger amounts (about 35 per cent). The nickel content of iron can be detected with a relatively simple test. The following reagents, obtainable from a drugstore, are required: hydrochloric acid, nitric acid (caution: causes burns!), citric acid, ammonia, dimethylglyoxime and 95 per cent alcohol. A small piece of the iron suspected of containing nickel, about the size of the head of a pin, is dissolved in a few cubic centimeters of hydrochloric acid, and heated to boiling with a few drops of nitric acid. A pinch of citric acid is added, the solution is cooled and cautiously neutralized with ammonia, and a few drops of dimethylglyoxime solution in alcohol are added. If everything has been done correctly, a bright scarlet-red precipitate appears in the presence of nickel. Many other criteria, ascertainable only by experts, will not be discussed here.

Fig. 53.—Iron meteorite from Toluca, Mexico: (*a*) polished unetched, (*b*) etched with acid. Scale about 2:1.

If the reader suspects, on the basis of the above criteria, that a stone or a metal object he has may be a meteorite, he need only send it or a small piece of it to the United States National Museum, Washington 25, D.C., for a free examination. The museum endeavors to purchase all genuine meteorites. However, he should not pin his hopes too high. Less than one in a hundred samples received turns out to be a genuine meteorite, but just this one, might, by the same token, be of particular value to science. Some of the objects most commonly mistaken for meteorites are pyrite and marcasite nodules; slugs, iron ores, and pig iron; heavy, dark, terrestrial rocks, and many other objects.

II. METEORITIC MATTER

WEIGHT AND SIZE

Weight and size of meteorites vary enormously. They range from finest dust to giants weighing 60 tons and measuring several meters.

The discovery of the fine dust was made possible by the fact that meteorites fell on frozen lakes—for instance the meteorite shower of Hessle in Sweden, on January 1, 1869, of which stones down to 0.07 grams were collected. In deep-sea sediments, too, very finely divided material of possibly meteoritic origin has been discovered. Figures 54–55 show a nickel-iron droplet and a silicate spherule, a so-called chondrule, discovered by the Challenger Expedition (1873–76) in the southern Pacific and Atlantic Oceans respectively. The remarkably high nickel content of deep-sea sediments has also been attributed to the finest fractions of meteoritic dust. Similar globules were separated magnetically from soil samples in the fall area of the Sikhote-Alin meteorite shower (see Fig. 56). They should not be confused with the minute iron spherules that are frequently found in dust, especially in industrial areas. The so-called Pultusk peas, thousands of which were found after the fall of the large meteorite shower near Pultusk, Poland, also weigh less than one gram each.

Pieces the size of a fist up to that of a head, rarely above 60 kilograms, predominate among the stone meteorites. Iron meteorites, on the other hand, are considerably heavier, masses of 50 to 100

Fig. 54.—Iron spherule from the deep sea, found in the southern Pacific. Magnified 110 times. (After Murray and Renard, *Deep Sea Deposits*.)

Fig. 55.—Chondrule from the deep sea, found in the southern Atlantic. Magnified 30 times. (After Murray and Renard.)

kilograms being fairly common. The iron meteorite of Treysa, Germany (Fig. 57), which fell on April 3, 1916, weighed 63 kilograms. The iron meteorite of Tocopilla, Chile (shown in Fig. 64, p. 80), weighed 75 kilograms. Their maximum dimensions were 36 and 40 centimeters, respectively. The largest iron meteorite observed to fall is one from the February 12, 1947, shower of Sikhote-Alin, halfway between Vladivostok and Khabarovsk. Its weight is

Fig. 56.—Nickel-iron spherules from soil samples of Sikhote-Alin. Magnified about 30 times. (Photographed by E. Krinov.)

Fig. 57.—Iron meteorite of Treysa, Germany. About one-eighth natural size. (After Richarz, in *Schriften zur Beförderung d. ges. Naturw.*, Marburg, 1917.)

1.745 tons. In Table 10, some of the largest stone meteorites and the ten largest iron meteorites are listed.

TABLE 10

I. STONES			
Place of Fall	Date of Fall or Find	Weight in Tons	Present Location
Norton County, Kansas	Feb. 18, 1948	1.073	Albuquerque and Nebraska
Long Island, Kansas	1891	0.564	Chicago
Paragould, Arkansas	Feb. 17, 1930	0.408	Chicago
Bjurböle, Finland	Mar. 12, 1899	0.330	Helsinki
Knyahinya, U.S.S.R.	June 9, 1866	0.293	Vienna
II. IRONS			
Hoba, South-West Africa	1920	60	At place of fall
Cape York, Greenland	1895	30.875	New York
Bacubirito, Sinaloa, Mexico	1871	27	Culiacán, Sinaloa
Willamette, Oregon	1902	14.175	New York
Chupaderos, Chihuahua, Mexico .	1852	14.1 & 6.77	Mexico City
Otumpa, Gran Chaco, Argentina .	1783 (1576)	13.6 & 4.2	London and Buenos Aires
Mbosi, Tanganyika	1930	12 or 26?	At place of fall
Morito, Chihuahua, Mexico	1600	11	Mexico City
Bendego, Bahia, Brazil	1784	5.36	Rio de Janeiro
Cranbourne, Victoria, Australia ..	1854	3.5	London

A few illustrations and comments will be given for this table. The heaviest stone meteorite, that of Norton County, Kansas, is the largest individual of a meteorite shower. It punched out a hole 3 meters in depth and survived the impact in one piece. This is also the case for the stone of Knyahinya, U.S.S.R., which belonged to a

FIG. 58.—Stone meteorite of Paragould, Arkansas. (From *Popular Astronomy*, 1930.)

Fig. 59.—Iron meteorite of the Hoba Farm, Southwest Africa. (After Schneiderhöhn, in *Centralbl. f. Min.*, 1931.)

shower totaling about 500 kilograms in weight. The stone of Paragould, Arkansas, also remained intact (Fig. 58).

When striking solid ground, stone meteorites often break up, for instance those of Long Island, Kansas (Fig. 65, p. 81), and Bjurböle, Finland. The impact hole of the latter is shown in Figure 8. Figure 59 shows the heaviest iron meteorite known to us, a find, that of Hoba Farm, South West Africa, near Grootfontein. Its dimensions are 2.95 × 2.84 × 1.25–0.55 meters. Its nickel content is 16.24 per cent so that here, all in one lump, is no less than 9.7 tons of nickel, along with 456 kilograms of cobalt. Business-minded people were about to refine it for these valuable metals, when the South African government declared the meteorite a national monument, thus saving it from destruction. As already mentioned, this iron is imbedded only 1.5 meters deep in the Kalahari limestone, protruding slightly from the ground. The surface of the meteorite is separated from the limestone by an intervening layer (Fig. 60) of iron shale mixed with calcareous material. It is the only iron meteorite, apart from the fragments of the giant meteorites, that has been found to be accompanied by iron shale. Just as in the other cases, this shale may well be a product of the impact. The meteorite of Cape York, listed in Table 10, is the heaviest individual iron of a meteorite shower. It is shown in Figure 61. The

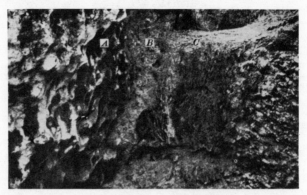

FIG. 60.—Iron meteorite of the Hoba Farm, Southwest Africa. (*A*) meteoritic iron, (*B*) iron shale, (*C*) limestone. (After Gordon, in *Mineralogical Magazine,* 1932.)

Eskimos called it "The Tent," another block of 3 tons, "The Woman," and finally the smallest one, of 0.436 tons, "The Dog." In more recent times, three additional blocks were found in that area. One of these weighs 3.4 tons and is now located in Copenhagen; the second weighs 7.8 kilograms, and the third, about 15 tons. The Eskimos seem to have known of these iron meteorites for a long time. They showed them to the American polar explorer, Peary, who brought them to the United States. The iron of Willamette has a most unusual shape (Fig. 62). The base of this cone-shaped meteorite contains numerous large, irregular, rounded

FIG. 61.—Iron meteorite of Cape York, Greenland. The hat in the lower right indicates the scale. (After Hovey, *American Museum of Natural History Guide Leaflet,* No. 26, 1907.)

Fig. 62.—Iron meteorite of Willamette, Oregon. (After Hovey.)

pits, large enough for small children to crawl into. It is not quite clear whether these cavities were formed by the fusion of readily fusible troilite as it passed through the atmosphere, or by weathering.* The iron ŏf Morito, known since 1600, bears the following chiseled inscription:

> Solo Dios con su poder
> Este fierro destruira
> Porque en el mundo no habra
> Quien lo pueda deshacer. A⁰. 1821.

Translated, this means approximately: "Only God with his might can destroy this iron, since there is no one in the world who could unmake it." Here, too, some fruitless attempts seem to have been made to utilize the iron. It is shown in Figure 63.

SHAPE

The shapes of meteorites differ widely. At the time of their entry into the atmosphere they are already fragments of random shape.

---

*[R. H. Johnson at General Electric Company has recently suggested that these cavities might have been produced by the flow of air at hypersonic velocities during the meteorites' passage through the atmosphere. Others believe that these cavities were present before the meteorite entered the atmosphere, or that they were caused by preferential rusting of lawrencite-rich regions.— Translator]

FIG. 63.—Iron meteorite of El Morito. (After Farrington.)

During fall they are sometimes further broken up. On the other hand, the ablation tends to smooth and round their contours.

The conical, approximately pyramidal form is particularly common. It is shown by the iron meteorite of Tocopilla, Chile (Fig. 64), and the stony meteorite of Long Island, Kansas (Fig. 65), the second largest known stone. Much rarer are the club- or column-like forms such as the iron of Babb's Mill, Tennessee (Fig. 66), or the strange ring shape as shown by the iron of Tucson, Arizona (Fig. 67). This sizable ring, weighing 688 kilograms, has a maximum hole diameter of 67 centimeters. We have already encountered irregular, jagged forms in the giant meteorite of Henbury, Australia (Fig. 22, p. 37). Among the smaller stone meteorites, irregular, rounded and lumpy forms predominate.

FIG. 64.—Iron meteorite of Buei Muerto, Chile.

FIG. 65.—Stone meteorite from Long Island, Kansas. (After Farrington.)

As we review all known meteorite shapes we can distinguish two groups, those in which no part of the surface differs from the rest in any special way, and those that seem to have a "front" and "rear" side that are plainly different. Meteorites of the latter group are called "oriented" meteorites. Evidently they did not change their position during their flight through the atmosphere, so that the front side was shaped differently from the rear side by the air stream. Figure 68 shows the beautifully oriented iron meteorite of Boogaldi, New South Wales. The front side is on the right. The Tocopilla iron meteorite (Fig. 64, page 80), also shows orientation, the peak or horn indicating the front side. An oriented stone meteorite, that of Rich Mountain, North Carolina, is shown in Figure 69. The front side is on top.

SURFACE FEATURES

Many meteorites show on their surfaces very characteristic shallow pits, and these are clearly visible in Figure 47, page 70, and Figure 70. Some people think that they are formed by the breaking-off of

FIG. 66.—The Babb's Mill, Tennessee, iron meteorite. It is nearly one meter long. (After Farrington.)

Fig. 67.—The Tucson, Arizona, iron meteorite. (After Hovey.)
Fig. 68.—The Boogaldi, New South Wales, Australia, iron meteorite. About one-third natural size. (After Liversidge, in *Proc. Roy. Soc. N. S. Wales*, 1902.)

portions of the meteorite and by the melting-away of readily fusible constituents, such as troilite, but a recent opinion is that they are the result of eddies in the supersonic flow of blazing hot, shock-compressed air. Corners and sharp edges are smoothed and rounded during the ablation process in the atmosphere. In the oriented meteorites, these cavities are particularly well developed

Fig. 69.—The Rich Mountain, North Carolina, stone meteorite. (After Merrill, in *Proc. U.S. Nat. Mus.*, Washington, 1907.)
Fig. 70.—The Cabin Creek, Arkansas, iron meteorite. (After Berwerth, in *Ann. naturhist. Hofmus.* Vienna, 1913.)

82

(a)   (b)

FIG. 71.—The Hvittis, Finland, stone meteorite: (a) front side, (b) rear side. About one-sixth natural size. (After Borgström, in *Bull. de la Comm. Géolog. de Finlande,* No. 14. 1903.)

on the rear side, while the front side is much smoother. Figure 71 shows the difference in smoothness quite plainly. From the degree of smoothing of fractured surfaces, one can infer that some meteorites have broken up late in their flight through the atmosphere. Owing to the shorter ablation time, the newly formed surfaces are smoothed less well than those that were present when the meteorite entered the atmosphere. Hence one can distinguish primary, secondary, and sometimes even tertiary surfaces.

All meteorites that were found soon after the fall and were not broken during impact are completely covered by a characteristic black, glossy, or dull fusion crust which, on many stones at least, differs strikingly in color from the lighter interior. This contrast is illustrated in Figure 72. The crust is usually paper-thin, on the average less than one millimeter thick, although it can occasionally reach a thickness of up to 10 millimeters. It is usually thinner on the front side than on the rear. In stone meteorites, it consists of black glass, and in iron meteorites, of black magnetic iron oxide (Fe_3O_4). The latter is rapidly destroyed by weathering, being replaced by a rust layer. That these crusts are actually produced by fusion is often indicated by the presence of flow structures that are quite clearly visible in Figure 68 (p. 82) and Figure 73. The molten material was swept to the rear by the air flow. The crust is

FIG. 72.—The Pohlitz, Germany, stone meteorite. A thin black crust covers the lighter interior. About natural size.

sometimes thickened considerably at the edge where the front and rear surfaces of the meteorite join.

CHEMICAL CONSTITUTION

As soon as the true nature of meteorites was recognized, people began to investigate them chemically in the greatest possible detail. Initially, the meteorites owed their interest to the fact that they represented the only material from outer space accessible to direct

FIG. 73.—The St. Marks, South Africa, stone meteorite. Note flow structure. (After Cohen, in *Annals, South African Museum,* 1906.)

laboratory investigation. More recently, a second reason has come to the fore. Geochemists, who are concerned with the material composition of the earth, believe that certain classes of meteorites have a composition similar to the material in the earth's interior, which may never be directly accessible to us. Thus meteorites provide an excellent means for testing some of the laws of the geochemical distribution of the elements deduced by laboratory studies and observations on the earth's surface.

A first important result of this thorough chemical investigation is that, up to now, *no chemical element has been found in meteorites that does not also occur on the earth.* Furthermore, no substances have been discovered that definitely require the presence of living organisms.

According to the most recent investigations, nearly all elements known on the earth occur also in meteorites. Of the ninety-two elements of the Periodic Table (not counting the transuranium elements), only the "missing" elements, technetium (Tc), promethium (Pm), astatine (At), and francium (Fr) have not yet been found in meteorites.

In their distribution in meteorites, the elements tend to concentrate in one or the other major constituent. One group is enriched in metallic nickel-iron, one of the main components of meteorites. In addition to iron (Fe) these include nickel (Ni), cobalt (Co), germanium (Ge), tin (Sn), gold (Au), and the platinum metals: ruthenium (Ru), rhodium (Rh), palladium (Pd), osmium (Os), iridium (Ir), platinum (Pt), and several others. Geochemists call these elements *siderophile* because of their preference for the iron melt (*sideros* = iron). A second group shows a great affinity for sulfur, and we therefore find them enriched in the iron sulfide (troilite) of the meteorites. Besides iron, this group includes copper (Cu), silver (Ag), zinc (Zn), cadmium (Cd), mercury (Hg), arsenic (As), antimony (Sb), and bismuth (Bi) as well as selenium (Se) and tellurium (Te) in addition to sulfur (S). These elements are called *chalcophile* (*chalkos* = ore). Finally, a third group shows strong affinity for oxygen and is enriched primarily in the meteoritic silicates. We call them *lithophile* (*lithos* = stone). To this group belong, in addition to oxygen (O), the alkalis lithium (Li), sodium (Na), potassium (K), rubidium (Rb), cesium (Cs), the alkaline earths beryllium (Be), magnesium (Mg), calcium (Ca) strontium (Sr), barium (Ba), radium (Ra), and also boron (B), aluminum (Al), scandium (Sc), yttrium (Y) and the rare earths, thorium (Th) and uranium (U); also carbon (C), silicon (Si), titanium (Ti), zirconium (Zr), hafnium (Hf), vanadium (V), niobium (Nb), tantalum (Ta), phosphorus (P), chromium (Cr), tungsten (W), manganese (Mn), and a few rare ones in addition. A fourth group that is very volatile in elemental or combined form, and is therefore concentrated in the atmosphere of celestial bodies, the so-called atmophile (*atmos* = air) elements, plays a very subordinate role in meteorites since the mass of the meteorite parent body seems to have been too small to retain these elements. Of these, only a few such as hydrogen (H), nitrogen (N), and the noble gases: helium (He), neon (Ne), argon (Ar), krypton (Kr), and xenon (Xe), have been detected (at trace levels) in meteorites.

Just as in the earth's crust, only a few elements occur in the meteorites in sufficient concentration to permit their determination by the classical methods of analytical chemistry. The great majority of elements are found in meteorites at concentrations of only a few grams per ton of meteoritic matter (one gram per ton corresponds to 0.0001 per cent), and it was first necessary to develop sufficiently sensitive analytical methods before this multitude of elements could be determined qualitatively and quantitatively in meteorites. For this purpose, spectrochemical analysis has been particularly useful, using X rays, visible, ultraviolet, or infrared light. These methods are based on the fact that the chemical elements emit radiations of characteristic wave lengths under suitable conditions. A simple experiment will illustrate this fact. If a steel needle is wiped with the bare thumb and forefinger and then inserted in the non-luminous flame of a gas burner, the flame turns yellow. The reason for this is that even the minute amount of sodium chloride contained in the trace of perspiration transferred from the skin to the needle is enough to impart to the flame the yellow color characteristic of the element sodium.

The light emitted by the elements is resolved into individual lines of different wave lengths by a prism (or a ruled grating) in the case of visible light, and a crystal in the case of X-rays. From the intensity of the characteristic spectral lines, one can infer the concentration of the elements that produced them. A disadvantage of these methods is their relatively low accuracy for some elements. Determinations can vary by as much as a factor of two, that is, the measured concentration of 0.001 per cent could just as well be 0.002 or only 0.0005 per cent. Sometimes the factor of error can be ten, and then we can only establish the order of magnitude of concentration, that is, whether the element occurs at levels of a few thousandths or ten-thousandths of 1 per cent.

In recent times another method of analysis has become available that makes it possible to determine a large number of trace elements to an accuracy of about 10 per cent at levels of only a few ten-thousandths of 1 per cent. This method involves making the trace elements in question radioactive by irradiation with neutrons in modern nuclear reactors and measuring the activity of the activated atoms of these elements by means of very sensitive physical methods. Such measurements were first done for gallium, palladium, rhenium, and gold, and have since been used for many other elements. The methods of analysis of very small amounts of gases have also been refined to an extraordinary degree so that amounts of only a few millionths of a cubic centimeter of helium, and even smaller amounts of the heavier noble gases, can be determined accurately.

Most of these modern methods involve very complicated operations (see, for example, Figure 75, page 92) so that they can only be carried out in specially equipped laboratories. The reason why people go to such trouble and expense is that the concentration of many of these rare elements in meteorites is frequently the only clue to the cosmic abundance of these elements. These measurements also permit us to determine the age of meteorites. The results obtained are of interest, not only for meteoritics, but to an equal degree for geochemistry, geophysics, cosmogony, and nuclear physics.

From measurements of this kind, the abundance data in the appendix have been obtained. The most important elements, in the order of their abundance, are oxygen, iron, silicon, magnesium, sulfur, calcium, nickel, aluminum, sodium, chromium, manganese, potassium, titanium, cobalt, and phosphorus. This order of abundance differs from that in the earth's crust. This is not surprising since the meteorites as a whole give us the average chemical composition of an entire planet, whereas on the earth we are only able to determine the average chemical composition of the outermost crust. The chemical composition of stone meteorites is most nearly comparable with the earth's crust, these meteorites consisting mainly of silicates with some nickel-iron and troilite. Such a comparison is shown in Table 11.

TABLE 11

Element	Chondrites (Per Cent)	Igneous Rocks (Per Cent)
Oxygen (O)	34.84	46.60
Iron (Fe)	25.07	5.00
Silicon (Si)	17.78	27.72
Magnesium (Mg)	14.38	2.09
Sulfur (S)	2.09	0.05
Calcium (Ca)	1.39	3.63
Nickel (Ni)	1.34	0.08
Aluminum (Al)	1.32	8.13
Sodium (Na)	0.68	2.83
Chromium (Cr)	0.25	0.02
Carbon (C)	0.1	0.03
Potassium (K)	0.084	2.59
Cobalt (Co)	0.08	0.002
Titanium (Ti)	0.066	0.44
Phosphorus (P)	0.05	0.12

We see from this compilation that the two most abundant elements, oxygen and silicon, occur in approximately the same ratio in both, whereas magnesium and iron predominate strongly in stone meteorites relative to the earth's crust. On the other hand, the latter is much richer in the alkali metals (sodium and potassium) as well as aluminum and calcium. Sulfur, which contributes substantially to the composition of stone meteorites, plays a very subordinate role in the earth's crust.

TABLE 12 *

	Per Cent		Per Cent
Iron (Fe)	89.7	Phosphorus (P)	0.18
Nickel (Ni)	9.10	Carbon (C)	0.12
Cobalt (Co)	0.62	Sulfur (S)	0.08
Copper (Cu)	0.04		

*[These values were determined in selected samples of virtually pure metal phase, as nearly free from troilite, schreibersite, and cohenite inclusions as possible. However, such inclusions, though very unevenly distributed, make up an appreciable part of the meteorite; for example, the average troilite content of irons has been variously estimated as 1.4 to 5 per cent, corresponding to 0.5 to 2.2 per cent sulfur. If these inclusions had been properly taken into account, the values for P, C, and S in Table 12 would have been much higher.—Translator]

Table 12 shows the average composition of iron meteorites according to a compilation by Buddhue. Evidently nickel occurs at about one-tenth the abundance of iron, and cobalt, in turn, at not quite one-tenth the abundance of nickel. All chemical elements not mentioned in Tables 11 and 12 occur in such extraordinarily low concentrations that many were not determined quantitatively until modern methods of analysis became available.

All these investigations have shown, nonetheless, that the *abundance of the elements in meteorites* follows the regularities known for the earth. Atomic physics has shown that the chemical elements can be arranged in a series in which every element has its strictly defined place or number. This number is also called the atomic number and is equal to the number of protons in the nucleus. The first element, with the atomic number 1, is hydrogen; that with the atomic number 92, the well-known element uranium. Elements with even higher atomic numbers have been produced artificially. Every atom consists of a nucleus containing almost the entire mass of the atom and an outer shell of electrons, that is, minute particles carrying a negative electric charge, circling the nucleus in various kinds of orbits. Since the atom as a whole is electrically neutral, the number of electrons is determined by the number of units of positive charge (protons) in the nucleus, the atomic number. Hydrogen therefore, has one electron, and uranium ninety-two electrons. The electron shell determines the chemical behavior of the elements and therefore also their geochemical character. But it has become apparent that the abundance of the different kinds of atomic

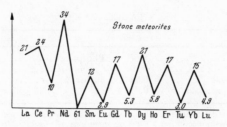

FIG. 74.—Abundances of the rare earth elements in meteorites. (After I. and W. Noddak, in Gmelin and Kraut, *Handbuch der anorg. Chemie.*)

species in the entire universe is largely determined by the atomic number. By and large, the abundance of various atomic species decreases with increasing atomic number. A few exceptions to this rule are known, but we shall not discuss them here. The elements hydrogen and helium, with atomic numbers 1 and 2, are consequently the most abundant ones, while uranium (atomic number 92) is a very rare element in the universe at large. A second trend is expressed by the so-called Harkins' rule: An element with even atomic number, say 18, 20, or 22, is more abundant than both its neighbors with odd atomic number, that is element 18 is more abundant than elements 17 and 19, element 20 more abundant than elements 19 and 21. Both rules were first observed in material of the earth's crust. The investigation of meteorites showed that they are also valid for extra-terrestrial matter.

A neat illustration of Harkins' rule is the *abundance of rare earth elements* in meteorites. The chemical behavior of this group of elements is so similar that they tend to remain together throughout all geochemical processes. Figure 74 shows their abundance as found by I. and W. Noddak. The elements of odd atomic number are always less abundant than both their neighbors of even atomic number. The total abundance of all elements with odd atomic number does not exceed 2 per cent in meteorites.*

The noble metal content in meteorites, which, as we saw, was

---

*[But it must be noted that meteorites are low in hydrogen, atomic no. = 1, while most stars are over 90 per cent hydrogen, which would make stellar abundances overbalanced on the side of the odd elements. We must make an exception of this element.—Translator]

one of the reasons for the intense search for giant meteorites, has been studied in detail. V. M. Goldschmidt predicted, from geochemical considerations, that iron meteorites should contain much higher levels of platinum metals than the earth's crust. Table 13, based on data by Goldschmidt and the American meteoriticist W. Nichiporuk, shows that this is indeed the case.

TABLE 13

Element	Atomic No.	Abundance (g/t)
Ruthenium (Ru)	44	7.0
Rhodium (Rh)	45	1.5
Palladium (Pd)	46	3.7
Silver (Ag)	47	0.1
Osmium (Os)	76	2.0
Iridium (Ir)	77	3.7
Platinum (Pt)	78	11.0
Gold (Au)	79	1.4

For example, the average content of platinum in meteorites is 0.001 per cent compared to an estimated concentration in the Earth's crust of only 0.0000005 per cent.

Even such rare elements as uranium and thorium have been determined by neutron activation analysis. In Table 14, their abundances in meteoritic irons are compared with those in stone meteorites and terrestrial igneous rocks. All abundances are expressed in units of grams per ton.

It is seen from this table that both elements are several orders of magnitude more abundant in stone meteorites than in irons,

TABLE 14

	Uranium (g/t)	Thorium (g/t)
Irons	10^{-3}–10^{-6}	10^{-3}–10^{-6}
Stones	0.01	0.04
Basic Igneous Rocks	1.1	3.9
Acid Igneous Rocks	4.1	13.0

but that their level in igneous rocks is more than two orders of magnitude higher still than in stone meteorites.

Gases have also been determined in meteorites. Representative averages for some gases are listed in Table 15.

TABLE 15

	No. of Analyses	Carbon dioxide CO_2	Carbon monoxide CO	Methane CH_4	Hydrogen H_2	Nitrogen N_2	Total Volume
Stones ..	12	3.77	0.24	0.20	0.50	0.09	4.80
Irons ...	9	0.21	0.67	0.02	1.67	0.24	2.81

Petroleum-like and bituminous hydrocarbons are also found in some meteorites. This fact is of interest in that it shows that the meteorite was not heated appreciably after its formation, even during its flight through the atmosphere, or else these hydrocarbons would have volatilized or charred. It is not necessary to assume biological processes for the formation of these hydrocarbons.

The helium and argon content is of particular interest, as we shall see in the chapter on the age of meteorites. The helium content of meteorites is small, and a particularly sensitive method had

Fig. 75.—Apparatus for the determination of very small amounts of helium and argon. (After Paneth, *Endeavour* 1953.)

to be developed in order to determine these minute amounts reliably. F. A. Paneth and his co-workers deserve credit for having developed such a method, permitting the determination of as little as one-millionth of a cubic centimeter of helium. Figure 75 shows the complicated apparatus needed for this purpose. By suitable experiments, Paneth was able to show that helium is retained tena-

TABLE 16

Name and Class		Helium in $10^{-6}cm^3/g$
Cape York, Greenland; Savik	Om*	$<$ 0.0002
"The Tent": see p. 78,		
Cape York, Greenland	Om	$<$ 0.001
"The Dog": see p. 78,		
Cape York, Greenland	Om	1.
"The Woman": see p. 78,		
Cape York, Greenland	Om	1.
Gibeon, South-West Africa; Lion River	Of	0.1
Gibeon, South-West Africa; Brit. Museum	Of	0.14
Gibeon, South-West Africa; Goamus	Of	0.15
Gibeon, South-West Africa; Amalia Farm	Of	0.2
Gibeon, South-West Africa; Gröndorn	Of	0.2
Gibeon, South-West Africa; Harvard	Of	0.36
Gibeon, South-West Africa; Amalia Farm	Of	3.4
Toluca, Mexico	Om	0.16
Toluca, Mexico	Om	6
Toluca, Mexico	Om	18.9
Braunau, Czechoslovakia	H	10.43
Staunton, Virginia	Om	0.85
Staunton, Virginia III	Om	19.
Staunton, Virginia V	Om	19.
Henbury, Central Australia, see p. 36	Om	0.88
Henbury, Central Australia, see p. 36	Om	5.
Canyon Diablo, Arizona, U.S.A. (see p. 31)	Om	1.
San Martin, Chile	H	1.76
São Julião de Moreira, Portugal, see p. 99	Ogg	2.
Seeläsgen, Poland	Og	2.
Santa Rosa, Colombia	A	3.
Nejed (Wabar) Central-Arabia: see p. 39	Om	4.
Cranbourne, Victoria, Australia	Og	5.
Wichita County, Texas	Og	11.5
N'Goureyma, French West Africa	Ob	14.
Seneca Falls, New York	Om	15.
Silver Crown, Wyoming	Og	17.
Nelson County, Kentucky	Ogg	20.
Lenarto, Czechoslovakia	Om	22.
Treysa, Germany, see p. 75	Om	26.5
Thunda, Queensland, Australia	Om	30.5
Mt. Ayliff, Cape Province, South Africa	Og	36.8
Morden, N. S. Wales, Australia	Iron	40

*Symbols: A = ataxite, H = hexahedrite, O = octahedrite,
b = brecciated, f = fine, g = coarse, gg = coarsest, m = medium.

ciously by nickel-iron even at high temperatures, whereas it is lost rather more readily from silicates.

Table 16 lists several results for the helium content of iron meteorites as determined by Paneth. It varies from less than 0.0002 to 40×10^{-6} cm³/g of meteorite. It is interesting that the helium content for different specimens of one and the same fall sometimes shows considerable variation, for instance, in the iron meteorites of Cape York, Greenland (see p. 78), Gibeon, South West Africa; Toluca, and Henbury (see p. 36). Since the helium in iron meteorites is produced by cosmic-ray bombardment, the samples of lower helium content were apparently located farther below the pre-atmospheric surface of the meteoroid.

The argon content is also quite low. The first measurements were made in 1951 by Gerling and his associates in the U.S.S.R., and many additional values have since become available. The concentrations found range from 1.6×10^{-6} to 7.1×10^{-5} cm³/g (see Table 21, p. 123).

While it is relatively simple to determine the concentrations of the elements in the individual phases of the meteorites—that is, in the metal, in the troilite, and in the silicate—this cannot be done with any certainty for the sum total of all meteorites. Unfortunately, these are the numbers of decisive importance for determining the abundances of the elements in the universe. The reason we cannot get reliable average concentrations is that we do not yet know with sufficient accuracy the relative proportions of the above-mentioned three meteoritic phases. V. M. Goldschmidt suggested that the proportions of the three phases: nickel-iron, troilite, and silicate, should be set as 2 : 1 : 10. For this reason, Goldschmidt, as well as I. and W. Noddack, and H. C. Urey suggested that the chondrites themselves constitute a good average of meteoritic material, since they already contain the three principal phases in approximately the above proportions. This idea has met with considerable success, although the chondrites seem to be low in several elements. The table in the Appendix gives the abundances for chondrites.

The *isotopic composition of the elements* in meteorites has also

94

been studied in some detail in recent years. We shall return to this topic in the chapter on the origin of meteorites.

METEORITIC MINERALS

The above chemical elements, either alone or combined as compounds or alloys make up the minerals of meteorites. Among them we find some that are also well known to us on the Earth. For example, the magnesium-iron silicates olivine $(Mg,Fe)_2SiO_4$, and bronzite $(Mg,Fe)SiO_3$; also the terrestrially common sodium-calcium feldspar, plagioclase, which is a mixed crystal of the sodium feldspar albite $(NaAlSi_3O_8)$, with the calcium feldspar anorthite $(CaAl_2Si_2O_8)$. Iron sulfide (FeS), occurring in meteorites as troilite, is quite common on the earth as pyrrhotite, although of slightly different composition. And finally, even native nickel-iron alloy is sometimes found on the earth, albeit rarely, though this is a major constituent of meteoritic iron. But the meteorites also contain minerals that have not yet been found on the Earth in a natural setting, though they can be made artificially without difficulty. These minerals are indicated by an asterisk in the table of meteoritic minerals at the end of the book.

We also find parageneses (occurrences of minerals in natural associations) that are not possible in the earth's crust, although the individual minerals occur on the earth. For instance, the siderophyre (see Table 19, page 116) of Steinbach, Germany, consists of native metallic nickel-iron, bronzite $(Mg,Fe)SiO_3$, and free silica in the form of tridymite (SiO_2). This paragenesis testifies that the concentration of oxygen at the place of formation of meteorites was low, much too low to permit the formation of an iron silicate. The degree of oxidation of the meteoritic magma must have been appreciably smaller than that of terrestrial magmas.

On the other hand, many minerals that play an important role on the Earth, for instance the minerals of the mica and hornblende groups, which are found singly or together in every granite or syenite, are completely absent in meteorites. Other missing minerals are the potassium feldspar orthoclase $(KAlSi_3O_8)$, the alkali aluminum silicates leucite $(KAlSi_2O_6)$ and nepheline $(NaAlSiO_4)$; the well-known rock salt (NaCl), and the terrestrially very common gypsum ($CaSO_4 \cdot 2H_2O$) as well as nearly all other minerals that normally crystallize from water solution. Water-containing weathering products which are so common on the Earth, particularly the clay minerals, are also absent from meteorites.* Water does not seem to have played a role during the mineral formation processes in most meteorites. The meteoritic minerals are nearly always fresh and undecomposed. From their chemical composition and their paragenesis we can conclude that the meteoritic minerals could have crystallized only from a fiery melt. In contrast to the terrestrial melts from which igneous rocks originated and which are known to us in molten state as volcanic lavas, the meteoritic melts seem to have been exceptionally poor in water. Only in the carbonaceous chondrite Staroe Boriskino, U.S.S.R. (fell April 20, 1930), chlorite- or serpentine-like minerals (hydrated magnesium-iron silicates) have recently been reported (see translator's note, above). Some data on the principal minerals of meteorites are given below.

Diamonds were first found in minute crystals in the stone meteorite of Novo-Urei, near Gorki, U.S.S.R. (fell September 4, 1886). Later they were also found in some specimens of the Canyon Diablo, Arizona iron, and in the iron of Magura, Czechoslovakia. These grains, usually only of microscopic size, sometimes show crystal faces of octahedra or hexakisoctahedra. They may be colorless, yellow, blue, or black. Figure 76 shows a presumed diamond grain from Canyon Diablo.

Graphite, the second form in which carbon occurs in nature, is found primarily in iron meteorites. It turns up either as minute flakes that are left behind after dissolution of the metal in acids, or in nodules rarely exceeding pea- or walnut-size. Sometimes it also appears in minute pseudocubic crystals called *cliftonite.* Some

---

*[In recent years the older (and mistrusted) observations of water-bearing minerals have been confirmed and extended. Gypsum, epsom salt ($MgSO_4 \cdot 7H_2O$), and the like have been found in the carbonaceous chondrites, together with certain odd clayey minerals which are unknown on earth. These meteorites include Staroe Boriskino, Mighei, Murray, Ivuna, Orgueil, etc.—Translator]

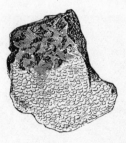

FIG. 76.—Diamond from the Canyon Diablo, Arizona, iron meteorite. Natural size about 0.7 x 0.3 mm. (After Moissan, in *Comptes rendus*, 1893.)

scientists believe that this cliftonite was originally diamond which was later converted to graphite, but this view has been criticized.

Meteoritic iron consists for the most part of two *iron-nickel alloys,* the nickel-poor *kamacite* and the nickel-rich *taenite*. We shall discuss these minerals in the section on the structure of meteorites.

Copper (Cu) occurs as a constituent of the nickel-iron in all iron meteorites, but only at levels of a few tenths to hundredths of 1 per cent. In the stone meteorites of Richardton, North Dakota; Garnett, Kansas; and the iron meteorite of Toluca, Mexico, it is reported to occur in native form. An alleged "meteorite" of zinc- and lead-containing copper (Eaton, Col.) is probably an artifact.

A silicon content of several atom per cent has been reported for the nickel-iron phase of the enstatite chondrites (see Table 19, p. 116).

Among the sulfides, *oldhamite,* or calcium sulfide (CaS), is not known as a natural terrestrial mineral, and has been found only in a few meteorites thus far. It is of light brown color, and translucent when fresh. In contact with water, that is, when the meteorite is left lying on the ground for some time after the fall, it oxidizes to gypsum ($CaSO_4 \cdot 2H_2O$). It contains a small amount of manganese sulfide (MnS). The occurrence of magnesium sulfide, which is likewise not known as a terrestrial mineral, in the stone meteorite Pesyanoe (near Kurgan, Siberia; fell October 2, 1933), has also been reported.

The most important sulfide is *troilite* (FeS) occurring as nodules

Fig. 77.—Troilite drops in the Mukerop, Southwest Africa, iron meteorite. Slightly reduced.

sometimes exceeding ten centimeters in diameter, or as plates or irregular grains. Figure 77 shows troilite droplets in the iron of Mukerop, and Figure 90, page 111, plate-like troilite crystals in the iron of Ilimaes, Chile. Newly fractured surfaces have a beautiful bronze-colored luster. Its chemical composition approaches the theoretical formula FeS very closely, whereas the terrestrial iron sulfide pyrrhotite usually has a sulfur excess. The nickel and cobalt content of troilite is low relative to that of the metal phase. The iron sulfides of stone and iron meteorites do not seem to differ from one another as a rule. There is probably some troilite present in every iron meteorite.

The third sulfide not known on the earth is *daubréelite*, an iron-chromium sulfide ($FeCr_2S_4$). It usually occurs together with troilite and is sometimes associated with the latter in parallel plates. Figure 78 shows troilite from the iron meteorite of Tocopilla, Chile, containing such daubréelite plates. In stone meteorites, daubréelite is rarer. In these, most of the chromium is combined with oxygen.

Schreibersite, an iron-nickel phosphide ($(Fe,Ni,Co)_3P$), is also known on Earth only as an artificial product. It occurs in meteorites in a great variety of shapes; for instance, in the iron meteorite of São Julião de Moreira, Portugal (Fig. 79); sometimes also in

FIG. 78 *(Right)*.—Parallel plates of daubréelite in troilite of the Tocopilla, Chile, iron meteorite. Magnified 8.5 times.

FIG. 79.—Schreibersite of hieroglyphic-like shape in the iron meteorite of São Julião de Moreira, Portugal. About natural size.

FIG. 80.—Thin platelets and needle (rhabdite) of schreibersite in the Tocopilla, Chile, iron meteorite. Magnified 5 times.

FIG. 78.

larger, well-developed crystals surrounding troilite nodules, or independently, often in radiating intergrowths in meteoritic iron. These two forms must have separated directly from the liquid melt. Schreibersite also appears in very thin platelets and in minute, needle-like crystals that have been named rhabdite. These are particularly common in the meteorites called hexahedrites and are ingrown regularly along certain planes of the iron crystals. This fact suggests that they separated from the iron after solidification, a process known as exsolution. Figure 80 shows a profusion of platelets as well as needles in the Tocopilla iron meteorite. The atomic ratio of (iron + nickel + cobalt) to phosphorus, which should be 3 : 1 according to the chemical formula, seems to vary somewhat, though the variation in the analyses may in part be caused by the difficulty of isolating very pure material. The content of nickel + cobalt varies within the approximate limits 10 to 45 per cent. Schreibersite is easily recognized in iron meteorites. It has a bright, silvery-white luster, it is hard and brittle, and breaks easily. It is insoluble in cold dilute acids. It is probably present in all iron meteorites, although sometimes in small amounts, and also in some stone meteorites.

Much less common is iron carbide, *cohenite* $(Fe,Ni,Co)_3C$ which, as the nickel- and cobalt-free cementite, plays such an important role in steel-making, and which also occurs on the Earth as a rare mineral. Externally, cohenite resembles schreibersite very strongly and can easily be confused with it. In a solution of copper chloride–ammonium chloride it is easily soluble, however (the carbon being left as a residue), whereas schreibersite is insoluble.

Lawrencite is ferrous chloride $(Fe,Ni)Cl_2$. Since it readily absorbs moisture from the air, one usually does not find it in solid form but as small droplets, with a green cast because of the nickel content. This mineral is a nuisance to meteorite collectors since the lawrencite-containing irons rust very easily.

Quartz (SiO_2) which is so common on the Earth, is exceedingly rare in meteorites. On the other hand, *tridymite,* another modification of SiO_2, is present in fairly substantial amounts in the meteor ite of Steinbach, Germany. In terrestrial rocks, tridymite is a fairly rare mineral.

Except for its occurrence in the fusion crust, *magnetite* (Fe_3O_4) is rare in meteorites. *Chromite* (Fe,Cr_2O_4) is fairly widely distributed, particularly in stone meteorites, although usually in small amounts. *Ilmenite* ($FeTiO_3$) is also rare.

Several members of the *feldspar group* occur in some stone meteorites in considerable quantity. They always belong to the plagioclases (calcium-sodium feldspars). Figure 92*a*, page 113, shows a microscopic picture of these feldspars. Their chemical composition corresponds to a content of calcium feldspar from about 25 to 95 per cent. A very unusual form, completely unknown on the earth, is maskelynite, a glass like a melted feldspar, with the approximate composition of labradorite (1 albite : 1 anorthite).

Magnesium-iron silicates such as *enstatite, bronzite,* and *hypersthene*—minerals having the formula $(Mg,Fe)SiO_3$, with enstatite the iron-poorest and hypersthene the iron-richest member of this series—occur in considerable amounts in some types of meteorites. Their content of ferrous oxide (FeO) varies between zero and about 25 per cent. The crystals of this series are rhombic. Chemically similar, but of monoclinic crystal form, is the series of solid solutions clinoenstatite-clinohypersthene.

The related calcium-magnesium-iron silicates are also rather common among the stone meteorites, such as *diopside,* $CaMg(SiO_3)_2$, *hedenbergite,* $CaFe(SiO_3)_2$, and *augite* (containing some alumina). However, the so-called alkali augites seem to be absent.

Next to nickel-iron, *olivine* $(Mg,Fe)_2SiO_4$ is the most common constituent of meteorites. It appears particularly in the pallasite group (compare Table 19, p. 116, and Fig. 91, p. 111) in large rounded or angular grains that sometimes show crystal faces. Figure 81 shows one such olivine grain with facets, from the Pallas iron (Krasnojarsk, U.S.S.R.) The ferrous oxide content of meteoritic olivines ranges from approximately zero to over 40 per cent.

Phosphates found in stone meteorites include *apatite* (calcium phosphate with fluorine and chlorine) and *merrillite* (sodium-cal-

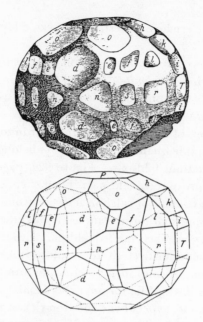

Fig. 81.—Olivine grain from the pallasite of Krasnojarsk, Siberia, showing faceting, an expression of the natural crystal facets. The sketch beneath it shows the completion of the facets to mutually intersecting crystal faces. (After Koksharov, in *Mater. Mineral. Russlands;* No. 6.)

cium phosphate) which is not known terrestrially. (But it seems that the so-called merrillite is identical with *whitlockite* [Ca$_3$-(PO$_4$)$_2$], a terrestrial phosphate mineral recently observed in a few chondrites.) Another phosphate mineral occurring only in meteorites is *farringtonite* (magnesium phosphate) which was found in the Springwater pallasite (Saskatchewan, Canada, found 1931).

The relative proportions of the meteoritic minerals in different kinds of meteorites are shown in Table 17, after Daly. The classification of meteorites is explained in Table 19.

STRUCTURE

Meteoritic minerals are intergrown to form more or less compact aggregates, which are the bodies known to us as meteorites. The texture of these intergrowths is often characteristic, enabling us to

TABLE 17

| Minerals | Irons* | Classes of Meteorite | | | |
		Pallasites	Mesosiderites	Achondrites	Chondrites
Nickel-iron	98.34	50.0	45.0	1.57	10.58
Olivine	..	48.0	1.5	12.82	42.31
Pyroxenes	..	..	30.6	62.25	28.91
Feldspars	..	..	16.4	20.75	11.82
Troilite	0.12	0.3	3.1	1.53	5.01
Schreibersite	1.12	0.2	2.6	0.40	..
Chromite	..	..	0.8	0.68	0.78
Cohenite	0.42	1.5	..	..	..
Apatite	..	..	..	..	0.67

*See footnote to Table 12

recognize the meteorites as such and to distinguish the various sub-classes from one another. We shall use the word *structure* to designate the intergrowth patterns of the meteoritic minerals. Structure depends very strongly on the composition of the meteorites, and we shall therefore consider separately the structures of the two main groups of meteorites, the irons and stones. In addition, we shall recognize a third group that represents a transition between the first two, and in which stony and metallic material contribute about equally to the composition.

We begin with the *structure of iron meteorites*. To make it clearly visible, the iron meteorite to be investigated is sawn across, or better still, a slice is cut off. This slice is then ground smooth and polished to a high luster. Many iron meteorites reveal their structure even at this point, but it shows up much more strikingly if the polished surface is etched with a very dilute solution of nitric acid in alcohol.

Surfaces treated in this manner reveal a variety of patterns. In some meteorites several groups of very fine parallel lines appear that cross each other in many directions. These lines are called "Neumann lines" after their discoverer. Occasionally one such line system stands out with particular clarity, as shown in the Tocopilla (Chile) iron meteorite in Figure 82. Actually, these lines represent cross-sections through very thin plates that penetrate into the main mass of the iron as so-called twin lamellae. They are formed by mechanical shock, and in some iron meteorites it can be shown that

Fig. 82.—Neumann lines in the Tocopilla, Chile, iron meteorite. One-quarter natural size.

they formed only during the collision of the meteorite with the Earth. Irons containing Neumann lines also have another characteristic property: they can easily be cleaved in three mutually perpendicular directions. Because of this cleavability along the faces of a cube (hexahedron), they are called *hexahedrites*. Chemically they consist of a uniform iron-nickel alloy, kamacite (see below). The parallel orientation of the Neumann lines throughout the Tocopilla meteorite and the cleavage planes which also pass through the specimen show that this entire iron meteorite represents a single crystal, 75 kilograms in weight! Actually, single-

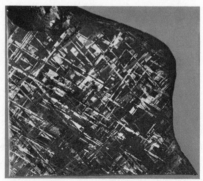

Fig. 83.—Widmanstätten pattern in the Mukerop, Southwest Africa, iron meteorite.

Fig. 84.—Widmanstätten pattern in the Duell Hill, North Carolina, iron meteorite. Magnified 4 times. (After Vogel, in *Abh. Ges. Wissensch.*, Göttingen, 1927.)

crystal hexahedrites of even greater weight have been found, as well as others that consist of kamacite crystals of varying orientations, differing widely in size (from a fraction of a millimeter to more than 10 centimeters in diameter).

Far more frequently, the meteorites show a coarser and more conspicuous structure after etching. Again, groups of parallel lamellae appear, crossing each other at various angles and enclosing between them areas of greater or lesser size. In contrast to the Neumann lines, these lamellae are frequently rather wide, about 0.2 to more than 2.5 millimeters. Figure 83 shows a structure of this kind. The characteristic pattern formed by these lamellae has been named the "Widmanstätten pattern" after its discoverer. When this pattern is examined under a microscope, or even a hand lens in the case of the coarser pattern, two different constituents can be distinguished: the nickel-poor, barlike kamacite (after the Greek word for shaft) which constitutes the main portion of the lamellae and is attacked fairly readily by acids, and the nickel-rich, ribbon-like taenite (after the Greek word for ribbon) which is much less readily attacked by acids. The taenite adjoins

105

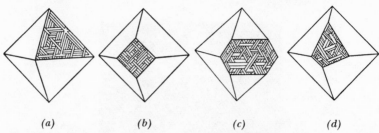

(a)   (b)   (c)   (d)

FIG. 85.—Arrangement of the bars of the Widmanstätten pattern as a function of the section angle: (a) section along octahedral face, (b) section along cube face, (c) section along the face of a rhombic dodecahedron, (d) section in an arbitrary direction. (After Tschermak, in *Lehrb. d. Mineralogie*, 1894.)

the coarse kamacite bars as a fine ribbon on both sides. The emergence of the pattern on etching is caused by the differences in acid resistance of the two nickel-iron alloys. The taenite plates of greater resistance stand out as fine ridges, whereas the kamacite bars are now recessed. If the etching is continued long enough, the relief becomes so great that the meteorite slice can be used directly for printing. Macroscopically, a third structural element can be seen: the fill-iron or *plessite* (after the Greek word for filling). It fills the spaces between the lamellae. The plessite is not an alloy of a new kind, however, as it merely consists of a most intimate mixture of kamacite and taenite. The structure of plessite can be so coarse that the two constitutents, kamacite and taenite, can be made out with a hand lens (the large gray areas with white dots in Fig. 84), or it may be so fine that it can be resolved into its constituents only at very high magnification. Macroscopically, the latter variety appears deep black after etching (the black areas in Fig. 84).

How did this regular arrangement of the lamellae come about? Further study shows that these iron meteorites consist of nickel-iron plates which give the appearance of lamellae in cross-section. These plates consist of kamacite, surrounded by a thin coating of taenite. They are arranged parallel to the four pairs of faces of an octahedron. As seen in Figure 85, an octahedron is a bipyramid composed of eight equilateral triangles. Pairs of opposite faces are parallel to one another, so that there is a total of only four different orientations for the face planes. We can build such an octahedron either by cutting it from a massive block of wood, or by gluing together small wooden boards at the angles of the octahedral faces, allowing them to interpenetrate each other somewhat. The latter method gives us a model of the Widmanstätten structure. If we now cut a plate from this model parallel to an octahedral face, as indicated in Figure 85a, we obtain a pattern similar to that of the iron meteorites. In cross-section, our boards will appear as bars, intersecting each other in this case at angles of 60°. These bars are surrounded on both sides by thin layers of glue, just as kamacite is surrounded by taenite. If the octahedron is sectioned at some other angle, the resulting pattern will have a slightly different appearance. Depending on the orientation of the cut, the bars will intersect at various angles. Several such cuts and the resulting patterns are shown in Figure 85. Exactly the same patterns are also observed in iron meteorites. If we happen to cut our slice parallel to an octahedral face, the lamellae will intersect at an angle of 60° (Fig. 85a). If the cut is parallel to a cube face (Fig. 85b), the angle between the lamellae will be 90°. Since we are usually not able to determine the orientation of the crystal faces before cutting, the cut will seldom have the favorable orientation of the two examples just discussed. Consequently, we are more likely to obtain angles such as those shown in Figure 85d, but from these angles it is possible to calculate, in turn, the orientation of the cut. Iron meteorites having this octahedral structure are called *octahedrites*. Further study has shown that sometimes lamellae

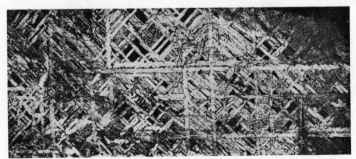

Fig. 86.—Arrangement of the kamacite bars according to faces of the octahedron *and* the cube. Tessera octahedrite of Bethany, Southwest Africa.

oriented according to the faces of the cube are present in addition to those oriented according to the faces of an octahedron (Fig. 86). This type is called "tessera octahedrite" (*tessera* = Latin for cube).

The octahedral structure can be brought out not only by etching but also by moderate heating of a well-polished surface. If a bright piece of steel is held in a flame for a short time it goes through a succession of bright "temper" colors due to oxidation. If this experiment is repeated with a slice of meteoritic iron, it too changes color. However, since the two nickel-iron alloys oxidize at different rates, the structure shows up as a beautifully colored pattern. This was the way Widmanstätten first discovered the pattern which now bears his name.

The formation of the octahedral structure probably occurred during and after crystallization of the nickel-iron from the melt by complicated processes that will not be discussed here. These processes are not yet fully understood, and it has not been possible up to now to reproduce completely this structure in the laboratory.

The orientation of the lamellae is usually uniform, even in the case of large blocks weighing hundreds of kilograms. This indicates that all of the block was once part of the same single crystal. In other irons, a system of lamellae is suddenly terminated at a

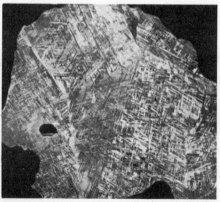

Fig. 87.—Polycrystalline iron meteorite from the Amalia Farm near Gibeon, Southwest Africa. Greatly reduced. (After Scheibe.)

108

Fig. 88.—Toluca, Mexico, iron meteorite. *Left,* before heating; *right,* after heating to 950° C for seven hours. Enlarged about 1.5 times. (After Berwerth, in *Sitz.- Ber. Akad. Wien,* 1905.)

sharp boundary, and on the other side of the boundary a second lamellar system of different orientation appears. Such a block thus consists of two, three, or even more individuals, depending on the number of lamellar systems. Figure 87 shows a section through such a multiple crystal (no less than eight systems of lamellae can be distinguished), from the Amalia farm near Gibeon, South West Africa. Here the parts are not arbitrarily put together, but again are intergrown in a regular manner.*

It is very significant that this octahedral structure, shown by the great majority of iron meteorites, is not stable at high temperature. If a slice of an octahedrite is heated for a fairly long period of time to 900 to 1000°C. (far below the melting point of nickel-iron), the structure can be obliterated completely. It changes to a finely granulated structure that persists even after cooling, as shown in Figure 88 for the iron meteorite of Toluca, Mexico. It is not possible to restore the octahedral lamellae in this reheated iron. Their appearance in the iron meteorites is therefore clear evidence that the octahedrites were not reheated for a prolonged period of time after their formation. Hence, even the flight through the atmosphere did not heat the meteorite to a high enough temperature long enough to effect the transformation to the granular structure.

A fine-grained structure rather similar to that obtained by heating is shown by a third group of irons, the so-called ataxites (without structure). Upon etching, neither Neumann lines nor a Wid-

---

*[Often the boundary between lamellar systems is marked by a line of troilite nodules, as in Bischtübe, Siberia—Translator]

mannstätten pattern can be seen, and they do not show cubic cleavage. This group is the hardest to distinguish from terrestrial artifacts. It appears, at least for some of these irons, that they owe this structure to reheating at a late stage of their history and that hence they are nothing but transformed octahedrites. Figure 89 shows an example of the ataxite structure.

The chemical analysis of both constituents, kamacite and taenite, has shown that the former has a nickel content of about 4.5 to

TABLE 18

Elements	Hexa-hedrites	Coarse Octahe-drites	Medium Octahe-drites	Fine Octahe-drites	Finest Octahe-hedrites	Nickel-poor Ataxites	Nickel-rich Ataxites
Iron (Fe)	93.59	91.22	90.67	90.53	86.75	91.07	79.63
Nickel (Ni)	5.57	7.39	8.22	9.00	11.65	6.88	18.85
Cobalt (Co)	0.66	0.54	0.59	0.57	0.61	0.54	1.01
Copper (Cu)	0.35	0.18	0.03	0.57	0.11	0.19	0.05
Phosphorus (P) ..	0.29	0.18	0.18	0.17	0.24	0.18	0.12
Sulfur (S)	0.06	0.08	0.09	0.08	0.63	0.06	0.08
Carbon (C)	0.19	0.21	0.08	0.61	0.01	0.08	0.10
All other elements	0.19	0.54	0.30	0.18	0.45	0.17	0.19
	100.90	100.34	100.16	100.19	100.45	99.17	100.03

7 per cent, about the same as the nickel-iron of hexahedrites, which consists only of kamacite. The taenite is much richer in nickel, its content of this element ranging from about 13 to more than 50 per cent. Consequently the proportions of the two alloys vary with the nickel content of the entire meteorite. The hexahedrites being lowest in nickel consist entirely of kamacite, while the octahedrites, with a variable nickel content of from 7 to about 15 per cent, contain both kamacite and taenite. The ataxites have a nickel content overlapping that of the other two groups, but it is nevertheless possible to recognize a nickel-poor and a nickel-rich ataxite group. Table 18, compiled by Buddhue, shows the variation of the content of nickel and several other elements with the structure. The smaller the lamellae of octahedrites, the more taenite and the more nickel they contain.

Apart from these structures, evidently formed by crystallization from a melt or by subsequent transformations in the solid state, there are others which in turn indicate a separation of phases al-

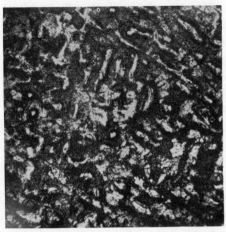

FIG. 89.—Ataxite structure of the Chesterville, South Carolina, iron. Enlarged about 70 times. (After Vogel.)

ready in the liquid state. This seems to have been the case for the spheroidal troilite nodules. Molten iron sulfide is miscible only to a limited degree with a phosphorus-containing iron melt and therefore separates in droplet form (see Fig. 77, page 98). Sometimes troilite has also separated in the form of thin plates that are frequently arranged in a regular pattern in the meteorite. Such

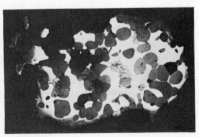

FIG. 90.—Reichenbach lamellae in the Ilimaes, Chile, iron meteorite. (After Tschermak, in *Denkschr. Akad. Wien,* 1871.)

FIG. 91.—Brenham, Kansas, pallasite showing apparent emulsion structure. About natural size.

111

lamellae are called "Reichenbach lamellae" after the meteoriticist Reichenbach. Figure 90 shows those in the iron of Ilimaes, Chile.

Such droplet formation is even more strikingly evident in the stony irons, meteorites representing the transition between irons and stones. Aside from nickel-iron and the ever present troilite and schreibersite, this class also contains substantial amounts of silicates. The most characteristic representatives of this group are the *pallasites* (named after the explorer Pallas). The metal, which shows a normal octahedral pattern, takes the form of a cellular, spongelike network, the cavities of which are filled with olivine grains of either rounded droplet-like or angular shape. In another group, the *siderophyres,* bronzite is found in place of olivine. The silicate grains can attain a diameter of more than a centimeter. Troilite and schreibersite are present in small amounts. Figure 91 shows an example of such a structure, the pallasite of Brenham, Kansas. It is a typical picture of a frozen emulsion. An emulsion is a dispersion of very fine droplets of one liquid in another that is immiscible with it, or miscible only to a limited degree. It is produced, for example, when we shake oil and water vigorously. Milk is an emulsion of butterfat droplets in an aqueous medium. In view of the large differences in density of the metal, sulfide, and silicate melts that constitute the immiscible liquids in the case of these meteorites, one would expect them to separate into three layers under the influence of gravity. The heavy iron melt would sink to the bottom, overlain by the sulfide melt and, at the top, by the relatively light silicate melt. Such a phase-separation seems to have occurred in the earth, and can be observed on a smaller scale in blast furnaces. That such a separation has not occurred in the case of the pallasites has been taken as an indication that the gravitational field was too small to overcome the viscosity of the melt. The lighter sulfide and silicate droplets were therefore not able to rise to the top and to coalesce into separate layers, in the way that the fat droplets in milk gradually rise to the top to form a layer of cream. Since a low gravitational field implies a low mass, the existence of pallasites has been regarded as evidence for the small size of the meteorite parent bodies. More recent calculations

112

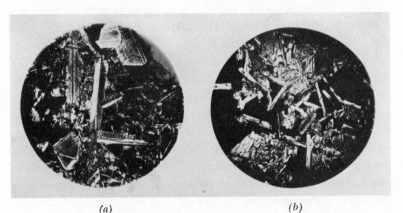

(a)   (b)

FIG. 92.—(a) Microscopic structure of the Juvinas, France, eucrite, (b) micro-scopic structure of the iron-bearing basalt of Ovifak, Greenland. Magnified about 40 times. (After Tschermak, *Mikroskop. Beschaffenheit d. Meteoriten*, 1883.)

show, however, that the lack of phase-separation in the pallasites must be attributed to other causes.

With increasing content of silicates, the metal phase becomes less and less continuous, until in the case of the stone meteorites proper, the metal occurs only as individual grains, usually of rather small size.

The *stone meteorites* can again be subdivided into two groups according to their structure. One group resembles certain terrestrial igneous rocks that are low in silica, not only in mineral content, but partly in structure. These rocks include some basalts (principal minerals: plagioclase and augite), the peridotites (mainly olivine), and the pyroxenites (mainly pyroxene). These meteorites are called *achondrites* since they lack a characteristic feature, the spherical chondrules (see below). Figure 92a gives a microscopic view of the structure of a eucrite (a subgroup of the achondrites) to be compared with a photomicrograph of a terrestrial basalt (Fig. 92b). The white bars are plagioclase, and the dark grains are pyroxene. The metal content of these meteorites tends to be very low.

But by far the greatest majority of stone meteorites belongs to a second group, the *chondrites,* that derive their name from the small spherical grains which characterize this class (Greek *chondros = grain*). These chondrules vary from microscopic size to the size of a pea or larger. Figure 93 shows chondrules of macroscopic size from the chondrite of Bjurböle, Finland. Usually only the smallest chondrules have a perfectly spherical shape. They vary greatly in number, size, and color. In some chondrites they are firmly imbedded in the ground mass and break with it when the stone is broken. In others, they can easily be pried loose from the matrix without breaking. Nearly all minerals of stone meteorites can form chondrules; those of bronzite or olivine are particularly common. Their internal structures can differ considerably, as shown by microscopic examination. Some consist of a granular aggregate; others have the so-called porphyritic structure (larger single crystals are imbedded in a finely granular or glassy ground mass). An eccentrically radiating structure is frequently found, particularly among the enstatite chondrules. Figure 94 shows a radiating and a porphyritic chondrule from the chondrite of Homestead, Iowa, magnified about forty times. Yet another struc-

Fig. 93.—Chondrules from the Bjurböle, Finland, chondrite. (After Merrill, in *U.S. National Museum Bulletin 149.*)

Fig. 94.—Chondrules in the Homestead, Iowa, chondrite. Magnified about 40 times. (After Tschermak.)

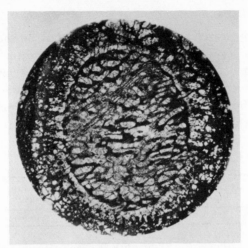

FIG. 95.—Olivine chondrules in the Mezö-Madaras, Rumania, chondrite. Magnified about 45 times. (After Tschermak.)

ture is shown in Figure 95, an olivine chondrule from the chondrite of Mezö-Madaras, Rumania. Larger chondrules sometimes enclose smaller ones or fragments of other chondrules. Some consist of a single crystal, others of several.

The structure of chondrites as a group varies from crystalline and granular to decidedly tuffaceous. A tuff is a rock consisting of volcanic ash and bombs. The chondrites nearly always contain small amounts of metal, occurring as jagged or rounded grains that reveal their presence by a brown rust halo after prolonged exposure to the atmosphere. Troilite is also present.

The question of the origin of chondrules and chondrites has not yet been settled conclusively. The decidedly tuffaceous nature of a number of these meteorites would seem to suggest an origin analogous to that of terrestrial tuffs. The chondrules themselves might be regarded as solidified droplets of a melt ejected during volcanic eruptions on the meteorite parent bodies. But true chondrules have never yet been observed in terrestrial rocks. Other workers have suggested that chondrules were formed by condensation of hot gases expelled from the sun during the formation of the solar nebula.

115

CLASSIFICATION

We have now learned the most important data on the chemistry,
mineral composition, and structure of the meteorites. Knowledge
of these three factors permits us to arrange the many diverse
types of meteorites into a system. This system was developed
mainly by the meteoriticists Rose in Berlin, Tschermak, Brezina,
and Berwerth in Vienna, and Prior in England. We have seen that

TABLE 19

I. Stones*

Silicates predominate over metallic constituents

	Principal Minerals	Examples
Chondrites		
Enstatite chondrites	Enstatite with some nickel-iron	Hvittis, Finland
Bronzite-olivine-chondrites	Bronzite, olivine, and some nickel-iron	Forest City, Iowa Pultusk, Poland
Hypersthene-olivine-chondrites	Hypersthene, olivine, and some nickel-iron	Holbrook, Arizona Mocs, Rumania
Achondrites		
Calcium-poor		
Aubrites	Enstatite	Aubres, France
Ureilites	Clinobronzite, olivine	Novo-Urei, U.S.S.R.
Diogenites†	Hypersthene	Johnstown, Colorado
Amphoterites‡ & Rodites .	Hypersthene, olivine	Rhoda, Spain
Chassignites	Olivine	Chassigny, France
Calcium-rich		
Angrites	Augite	Angra dos Reis, Brazil
Nakhlites	Diopside, olivine	Nakhla, Egypt
Eucrites§ and Shergottites	Clinohypersthene, anorthite; the same with maskelynite instead of plagioclase	Stannern, Czechoslovakia Shergotty, India
Howardites"	Hypersthene, olivine, clinohypersthene, anorthite	Pasamonte, New Mexico
Siderolites#		
Transitional between stones and irons; silicates predominant		
Lodranites	Bronzite, olivine, nickel-iron	Lodran, India
Mesosiderites	Bronzite, olivine, nickel-iron	Estherville, Iowa
Grahamites**	Bronzite, olivine, nickel-iron, with plagioclase	Vaca Muerta, Chile

	Principal Minerals	Examples
Lithosiderites# Transitional between irons and stones; metal predominant		
Siderophyres††	Bronzite, tridymite, troilite, nickel-iron	Steinbach, Germany
Pallasites‡‡	Olivine, nickel-iron troilite	Krasnojarsk, U.S.S.R.
Hexahedrites	Kamacite, troilite, schreibersite	Braunau, Czechoslovakia
Octahedrites (with coarsest, coarse, medium, fine, and finest lamellae)	Kamacite, taenite, troilite, schreibersite	Sikhote-Alin, U.S.S.R., Ogg. Canyon Diablo, Arizona, Og. Toluca, Mexico, Om. Gibeon, S. W. Africa, Of. Bristol, Tennessee, Off.
Ataxites		
Nickel-poor ataxites	Nickel-iron	Chesterville, S. Carolina
Nickel-rich ataxites	Nickel-iron	Babbs Mill, Tennessee Hoba, S. W. Africa

*May be subdivided further according to color (white, intermediate, gray, black), structure (crystalline, brecciated, veined), and peculiarities of composition (carbonaceous).
† After Diogenes of Apollonia
‡ After Greek amphoteroi = containing both (olivine and hypersthene)
§ After Greek eucritos = plain (mineral content easily determinable because of large grain size).
″ After the chemist Howard
After Greek sideros = iron, lithos = stone
** After the chemist Graham
†† After Greek sideros = iron, phyrao = knead
‡‡ After the explorer Pallas

the meteorites can be divided into two principal groups: irons and stones. On the basis of their structure and chemistry, the irons can be divided further into hexahedrites, octahedrites, and ataxites; the stones, into achondrites and chondrites. Transitional types exist between these two main groups. They can either be assigned to one or the other of the two main groups, or classified separately as a third group. Aside from these main groups, Table 19 also includes several subgroups.

III. ORIGIN AND FORMATION OF METEORITES

AGE

For a discussion of the topics given in the heading to this chapter, and for cosmogony in general, a knowledge of the age of meteorites is of particular importance. We may first ask: When did meteorites begin to fall on the earth? The oldest meteorite whose fall has been observed and of which material has still been preserved is the stone that fell on November 16, 1492, in Ensisheim, Alsace, as we saw in the section on "Historical Facts Concerning Meteorites." Many of the finds appear to be much older. The "Hadshar al Aswad," in the Kaaba at Mecca, which is presumably a stone meteorite, was already worshiped by the Arabs some time before the era of Mohammed (about A.D. 600). As mentioned above, the Canyon Diablo iron meteorite has been estimated to be at least five thousand years old, and the iron from the Oesel crater-field is presumably of similar age. A high age, by human standards at least, is indicated also by the very name for iron in several ancient languages, for it clearly refers to its extra-terrestrial origin (see p. 61). The authentic meteorite material which is presently in our hands has thus reached the earth during the recent, or at the earliest, during the upper Pleistocene (time of the last glaciation).

We may now ask whether there are any signs that meteorites fell on the earth during even earlier geologic times, that is, are there any "fossil meteorites"? The iron of Sardis, Burke County, Georgia,

118

was found in 1940, in strata believed to be of Middle Miocene age. While an oil well was being drilled in Zapata County, Texas, in 1930, an iron meteorite was located at a depth of 165 meters, in layers of undoubted Eocene age. Oxidized metallic spherules of presumably meteoritic origin have been found in deep sea cores from the Atlantic, reaching down to strata of Tertiary age. A further indication for meteorite falls in earlier times is given by the occurrence of the so-called moldavites (see Appendix) in strata of Middle Tertiary age (Helvetian) from Czechoslovakia, and the bediasites found in Lower Tertiary strata in Texas and Georgia. Both of these varieties of tektites are silica-rich glasses, which, according to the investigations in the Mineralogical Institute at the University of Jena, probably are not meteorites themselves, but are connected in some way with the fall of giant meteorites.

In older geologic formations, no signs whatsoever of the presence of meteorites have been found, and we must ask ourselves whether this means that no meteorites fell in these early times—this would be a most significant finding—or whether they were not preserved, or whether we simply have not yet discovered them. That stone meteorites cannot be found in strata of great geologic age is not surprising, in view of their low resistance to decomposition and the similarity to terrestrial material of their weathering products. But the situation is different in the case of iron meteorites, particularly the large ones. Even in the case of complete oxidation to the relatively immobile oxides and hydroxides, a geochemically unusual concentration of elements such as iron, nickel, cobalt, noble metals, etc., would have attracted people's attention had it occurred more frequently. If we consider, moreover, that since the onset of modern coal mining, some fifty to fifty-five billion tons of coal have been mined, all of which have passed through the hands of people with a professional familiarity with stones, it is certainly remarkable that ancient meteoritic material has never been found or described up to now. For this reason, some geologists have denied the existence of fossil meteorites, which leads to the remarkable conclusion that the Earth has only recently been subjected to meteorite bombardment. However, this conclusion is hardly justified if for no other reason than that only about one-hundredth of the Earth's surface is under observation, while the accessible portion of the former surface exposed during past geologic periods is several orders of magnitude smaller still.

Fortunately, we are in a position to establish *the absolute age of meteorites* by other methods. Just as in the case of terrestrial minerals and rocks, it can be determined by means of the natural radioactive decay of certain elements. Let us illustrate this in terms of the uranium-helium method. Several chemical elements are known to decompose spontaneously to other elements. This decay cannot be prevented by any means whatsoever. The most widely known of these radioactive elements is radium. But this is itself a decay product of its parent element, uranium, and decays further into yet another element, radon, which in turn decays further. The two stable end products which do not decay are Pb^{206}, and He^4. Observation has shown that the decay of one atom of uranium produces one atom of lead and eight atoms of helium.

If we are sufficiently certain that the helium found in a mineral, a rock, or, in our case, a meteorite, was produced by radioactive decay, and if, moreover, no helium has been lost from the meteorite since its formation, we can calculate from the observed number of helium atoms the number of uranium atoms that must have decayed to produce it. If we now measure the present uranium content of the meteorite, then it becomes possible to calculate the time required for the formation of the observed amount of helium, since it is known from laboratory experiments at what rate this decay takes place. The ratio of helium to uranium is proportional to the elapsed time. It is possible, of course, to calculate the age from the number of newly formed lead atoms. This method is difficult to apply, however, since the lead content of meteorites is small, and only a portion of this lead is produced by radioactive decay of uranium.

Unfortunately, the large body of data on the helium, uranium, and thorium content of iron meteorites accumulated by Paneth and his associates could not be used for age determinations as had been assumed initially. In 1947, C. A. Bauer suggested that at least part of the helium was formed not by radioactive decay, but by action of cosmic rays on the iron nuclei in the meteorite. He pointed out that this process would produce some helium of mass 3, whereas radioactive decay would produce only helium of mass 4. Paneth investigated the helium in a number of meteorites and found that helium[3] was indeed present, in amounts up to more than 30 per cent of the total helium. Later Reed, Hamaguchi, and Turkevich established that the uranium content of iron meteorites was much too low ($10^{-9} - 10^{-12}$ g U/g) to account for more than a minute fraction of the helium[4]. This implies that most of the helium in iron meteorites is produced by the action of cosmic rays during the meteorite's flight through interplanetary space.

Although it thus became evident that the helium was produced by a process altogether different from that assumed originally, it was still possible to use the helium data for age determinations. If the rate of production of helium is known (for example, from

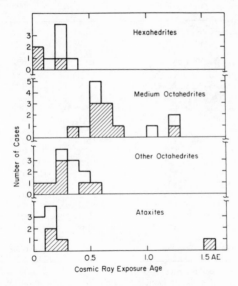

Fig. 96.—Cosmic-ray exposure ages of iron meteorites. The shaded values are somewhat more reliable than the unshaded ones. From this limited set of data, it seems that the medium octahedrites tend to be older than the other classes, but this conclusion is far from certain. (From G. P. Kuiper and B. M. Middlehurst [eds.], *The Solar System,* Vol. IV [Chicago, 1963].)

measurement of a short-lived radionuclide that is also produced by cosmic rays), one can calculate how long the meteorite was bombarded by cosmic rays. Since cosmic rays cannot readily penetrate iron for more than a meter or so, this "cosmic-ray exposure age" gives the time during which the meteorite has existed as a fragment no more than a few meters in size. The cosmic-ray exposure ages of iron meteorites vary all the way from eight million to more than one billion years* (Table 20 and Fig. 96). It is not clear whether these dates refer to the actual breakup of the meteorite parent bodies or merely to later breakups of the larger primary fragments.

More recently, cosmic-ray exposure ages have also been determined from the Ne^{21}, Ar^{36}, and Ar^{38} content, since these nuclides,

TABLE 20

No.	Meteorite	Class*	He^4 $10^{-6}cm^3/g$ at STP	He^3/He^4	Cosmic-ray Exposure Age (million years)
1	Aroos, U.S.S.R.	C. Oct.	25.4	0.258	530
2	Braunau, Czechoslovakia	Hex.	0.34	0.103	8
3	Grant, N. Mexico ...	F. Oct.	19.9	0.276	590
4	Sikhote-Alin, U.S.S.R.	C. Oct.	1.65	0.231	220
5	Treysa, Germany ...	M. Oct.	21.0	0.326	310
6	Kunashak, U.S.S.R...	Ch.	1.5	0.033	2.8
7	Beardsley, Kansas ..	Ch.	13.6	0.0067	6
8	Bjurböle, Finland ..	Ch.	16.7	0.010	12
9	Holbrook, Arizona ..	Ch.	18.3	0.015	18
10	Richardton, N. Dak.	Ch.	15.1	0.022	22
11	St. Michel, Finland..	Ch.	6.25	0.050	21
12	Ensisheim, Alsace ..	Ch.	13.4	0.022	20
13	Farmington, Kansas .	Ch.	1.7	0.003	0.2
14	L'Aigle, France	Ch.	9.4	0.015	9
15	McKinney, Texas ...	Ch.	1.3	0.041	4
16	Pultusk, Poland	Ch.	13.0	0.0077	7
17	St. Marks, S. Africa..	Enst. Ch.	6.0	0.0022	1
18	Sioux Co., Nebraska .	Ho	54.0	0.0044	16
19	Stannern, Czechoslovakia	Eu	79.2	0.0045	24

* C. Oct. = coarse octahedrite, Hex = hexahedrite, F = fine, M = medium, Ch = chondrite, Enst. Ch. = Enstatite chondrite, Ho = howardite, Eu = eucrite.

*[Urey has proposed the term "aeon" (AE) as a substitute for "billion years." Thus 1 AE = 10^9 years, without any ambiguity as to whether the British or American billion is meant.—Translator]

like He³, are produced almost exclusively by cosmic rays. Most ages in Table 20 are an average of several such estimates.

The uranium content of stones is much higher (1×10^{-8} g U/g in chondrites, and up to 10^{-7} g U/g in achondrites). Hence a large part of the helium is due to radioactive decay of uranium, as shown by the low He³/He⁴ ratios in Table 20. The He³ content can once again be used to calculate cosmic-ray exposure ages, which turn out to be considerably shorter than those for the irons. The reasons for this difference are not well understood.

The ages determined by the argon method, based on the decay of potassium⁴⁰ to argon⁴⁰, are listed in Table 21: numbers 1–4 were determined by Gerling and co-workers; numbers 5 and 6, by Wasserburg and Hayden; numbers 7–13, by Geiss and co-workers,

TABLE 21

No.	Meteorite and Class*	Potassium (Parts per million)	Argon $10^{-6}cm^3/g$ at STP	Potassium-Argon Age AE	Uranium-Helium Age AE
1	Kunashak, U.S.S.R., Ch., gray part	650	2.4	0.72	0.55
2	Kunashak, U.S.S.R., Ch., black part	900	6.5	1.2	...
3	Pervomaisky, U.S.S.R., Ch., gray part	800	2.5	0.65	0.63
4.	Pervomaisky, U.S.S.R., Ch., black part	1,250	15.2	1.8	0.94
5	Beardsley, Kansas, Ch.	1,010	71.3	4.3	3.6
6	Forest City, Iowa	831	53.4	4.15	4.1
7	Bjurböle, Finland, Ch.	840	60.5	4.32	4.2
8	Holbrook, Arizona, Ch.	880	66.5	4.4	4.4
9	Marion, Iowa, Ch.	870	54.0	4.08	2.35
10	Mocs, Rumania, Ch.	870	62.0	4.30	2.4
11	Modoc, Kansas, Ch.	830	55.0	4.18	3.0
12	Richardton, N. Dak., Ch..	830	54.0	4.15	3.8
13	St. Michel, Finland, Ch.	910	54.0	4.00	1.9
14	Chateau Renard, France, Ch.	835	1.93	0.51	0.3
15	Ensisheim, Alsace, Ch.	199	8.0	3.48	3.75
16	Farmington, Kans., Ch.	850	3.55	0.83	0.71
17	L'Aigle, France, Ch.	903	50.8	4.03	3.0
18	McKinney, Texas, Ch.	826	15.0	2.32	0.45
19	Pultusk, Poland, Ch.	770	40.8	3.93	3.42
20	St. Marks, S. Africa, Ch.	757	36.6	3.78	2.45
21	Sioux Co., Nebr., Ho.	326	11.4	3.26	2.95
22	Stannern, Czechoslovakia, Eu.	690	30.0	3.79	3.6

* Ch = chondrite, Ho = howardite, Eu = eucrite

and 14–22, by Zähringer and co-workers. The last column gives uranium-helium ages, calculated from the total He[4] content in Table 21 after correction for cosmic-ray-produced He[4]. A plot based on a larger number of measurements is shown in Figure 97. Comparing the figures in Tables 20 and 21, it becomes evident that the cosmic-ray exposure age of a given meteorite is always much shorter than the potassium-argon or uranium-helium ages. Evidently, the collision or breakup measured by the exposure age happened quite late in the meteorites' history. The potassium-argon and uranium-helium ages, on the other hand, measure the time since the meteorite cooled to a low enough temperature to retain argon[40] and helium[4], that is, no more than, say, 100°C at the most. Figure 97 shows that in many cases this cooling happened shortly after the formation of the meteoritic minerals (i.e., 4.5 AE ago, according to no less than three different dating methods),

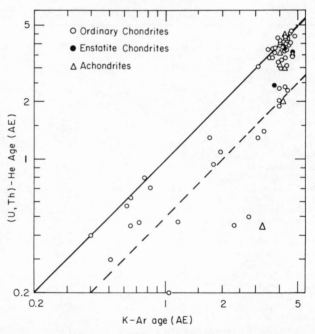

Fig. 97.—Comparison of uranium-helium and potassium-argon ages of stone meteorites. (From Kuiper and Middlehurst [eds.], *The Solar System*, Vol. IV.

although it seems to have occurred as recently as a few hundred million years ago in some cases.

Laboratory experiments show that He^4 is lost more easily at a given temperature than Ar^{40}. Hence the *concordant* potassium-argon and uranium-helium ages in Table 21 imply fairly rapid cooling through the temperature range where helium is lost but argon is not. Alternatively, it is possible that some of these meteorites were reheated strongly at some stage in their history, perhaps by a collision, so that the amounts of both gases that had accumulated up to that time were lost completely. This explanation may apply especially to the meteorites with ages less than 4.5 AE.

The meteorites with *discordant* potassium-argon and uranium-helium ages, on the other hand, have either cooled slowly through the lower end of the temperature range where helium is lost, or were reheated slightly at a later time, so that helium was lost preferentially.

It has also been observed that meteorites consisting of two visually distinct fractions sometimes show discordant ages; for example, the gray fractions of the chondrites of Kunashak and Pervomaisky compared to the black ones. Further work will be needed to determine whether this difference is real.

It is also of interest that the meteorites are older than the oldest known rocks on the earth (3 AE), although their age agrees with the estimated time of separation of the earth's crust from the core and mantle (4.5 AE).

ORIGIN

What conclusions on the origin and evolution of meteorites can be drawn from all this material? This is the last and most important question we shall ask ourselves.

As we saw in the historical review, the view that the meteorites are terrestrial bodies, such as ejecta of volcanoes, has been ruled out since the days of Chladni. According to modern views on the nature and structure of the rocks that can be expected on the surface of the earth, a terrestrial origin for meteorites is out of the question. Only for certain types of achondrites might this perhaps

125

be possible, but these meteorites fit so well among the other meteorites that a separate mode of origin for them is hard to justify. Isotope measurements provide independent evidence against a terrestrial origin. The meteorites are thus undoubtedly extra-terrestrial objects.

It is somewhat harder to determine whether they belong to our solar system or whether they reach us from interstellar space. This question is of great importance for our views on the uniformity of composition of the universe.

Let us first ask what relationship they have to shooting stars and fireballs, objects from which we receive only light signals and that do not reach the surface of the earth. All observations indicate that shooting stars, fireballs, and meteorites do not differ from one another in any fundamental way. It is true that the statistics of meteorite falls (p. 58) showed no correlation between individual meteorites and the so-called meteor showers. But apart from these showers, there are many sporadic shooting stars which, according to the intensity of their light output, grade smoothly into fireballs. These in turn show all intermediate transitional stages to meteorites. It thus appears that these three phenomena differ primarily in mass. Only with a mass greater than a certain value can extra-terrestrial bodies survive the rough treatment which they suffer after entry into the atmosphere. If their mass is too small, they burn up to vapor and smoke. The lack of a correlation between meteorites and meteor showers is probably due to the fact that the material of the showers has been subdivided so finely that not a single individual of the shower has the minimum mass needed to penetrate the earth's atmosphere.*

The orbit determinations made by astronomers for shooting stars, fireballs, and meteorites formerly seemed to indicate that they come primarily from interstellar space. The observational data on which these calculations were based are so inaccurate,

---

* [According to current views, meteor showers and many sporadic meteors are derived from comets, whereas most, if not all fireballs and meteorites are derived from asteroidal debris.—Translator]

however, that it would seem very unwise to assume an interstellar origin for all meteorites on the basis of these calculations alone. More recent orbit determinations for relatively well-observed falls; the recalculation of orbits for older falls, for example Pultusk; the results of a new observational method, radar; and, finally, the photographically determined orbit of the Příbram meteorite (p. 3), all seem to indicate that the meteorites belong to the solar system. Thus the astronomical findings have at last come to agree with the views of mineralogists and chemists whose investigations have always suggested an origin within the solar system for the meteorites.* In view of the great importance of this question, the value of exact trajectory determinations by laymen should again be emphasized.

For the large iron meteorite which produced the shower of Sikhote-Alin, the Soviet astronomer Fesenkov calculated an orbit showing a relation between this meteorite and the asteroids. This is a very significant result. The orbit is shown in Figure 98.

The times of fall of meteorites may be cited as further evidence for an origin of meteorites within our solar system. In our discussion on page 58, we saw that about two-thirds of all meteorites of known fall date have fallen between noon and midnight. They must have orbited the sun in the same direction as the earth. For the remaining one-third, with fall times from midnight to noon, it is not necessary to assume, as already pointed out, that they moved in the opposite direction. They could also have been overtaken by the earth. It is not yet possible to decide between these two alternatives.

The age determinations of meteorites also seem to point to an origin within the solar system. None of the meteorites investigated turned out to be older than four to five AE; an age that is of the same order of magnitude as that of the oldest terrestrial rocks. Of

---

*[It can also be shown that the Earth is so small a target for objects coming from interstellar space that even the most optimistic assumptions for the ejection of meteorites from other planetary systems would lead one to expect no more than one extra solar system meteorite for every million or so solar system ones. With fewer than ten meteorites recovered each year, we would have to wait 100,000 years, on the average, for an extra-solar-system one to fall.—Translator]

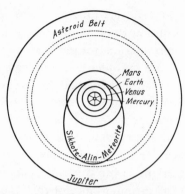

Fig. 98.—Orbit of the Sikhote-Alin meteorite. (After V. G. Fesenkov.)

course, this argument is not entirely conclusive, since there are many stars that have approximately the same age as the sun.

We saw in the section on the chemical composition of meteorites that the abundance of the elements in meteorites agrees rather well with that in the earth and follows the same regularities. By and large, this agreement extends even to the isotopic composition of the elements. Nuclear physics has shown that the chemical elements only rarely consist of a single kind of atom. The majority consist of two, three, or even more kinds of atoms, identical in chemical behavior but differing in mass. These different atomic species of a single element have been called "isotopes." Iron, for example, with an atomic weight of 55.85, consists of four isotopes of masses 54, 56, 57, and 58 in such proportions that the above atomic weight results. Nickel (atomic weight 58.71) is a mixture of no less than five different isotopes of masses 58, 60, 61, 62, and 64, whereas cobalt consists only of a single species of mass number 59. Many highly accurate mass spectrometer measurements have shown that the proportions of the isotopes in the chemical elements on the earth vary with locality only to a very minute extent. In the same manner the isotopic composition of the meteoritic elements has been investigated, with the remarkable result that while there are characteristic deviations from the terrestrial isotopic ratios in a few cases, these deviations are exceedingly small and in most instances well within the range of variation observed

128

on the earth. Table 22 shows the isotopic ratios of several terrestrial and meteoritic elements. The mass numbers are indicated on the upper right of the chemical symbols, for instance, $He^3 =$ helium isotope of mass 3; $He^4 =$ helium isotope of mass 4, etc.

TABLE 22

Element	Isotopes	Meteorites	Earth
Helium He	$He^3 : He^4$	$3 \times 10^{-4} - 0.33$	$0.1 \times 10^{-7} - 120 \times 10^{-7}$
Carbon C	$C^{12} : C^{13}$	$89.6 - 91.7$	$88.1 - 94.1$
Oxygen O	$O^{16} : O^{18}$	$495.5 - 495.6$	$491.1 - 504.0$
Sulfur S	$S^{34} : S^{33} : S^{32}$	$4.55 : 0.79 : 100$	$4.57 : 0.80 : 100$
Iron Fe	$Fe^{54} : Fe^{57}$	$2.69 - 2.78$	$2.60 - 2.81$

These figures indicate a near-identity of meteoritic matter with that of the earth, thus again suggesting a solar system origin for these bodies. According to current views, the isotopic composition of the elements is expected to vary from place to place within the universe. Still, it is possible that such variations are quite small in most instances, so that this is not a foolproof criterion for a common origin. Again, this emphasizes the importance of studying the meteorites and their fall phenomena most thoroughly. Perhaps these investigations will eventually give us an unequivocal answer to the fundamental question of the material composition of the universe.

FORMATION

Many different hypotheses on the formation of meteorites have been proposed. Immediately after Chladni's views had become accepted, it was assumed that meteorites were ejecta from lunar volcanoes. Their chemical composition and structure speak against this view and also against the hypothesis that the meteorites consist of the last residue of primordial matter left over after the formation of the Earth and the Moon, which is supposed to have coagulated gradually into larger chunks, the meteorites. The well known Swedish scientist Svante Arrhenius assumed that stars eject very finely divided matter, which coagulates to dust and finally to meteorites.

The hypothesis which appears most likely in the light of our present-day knowledge is that the meteorites are fragments of one or several celestial bodies. This view was first expressed toward the end of the last century by the meteoriticists Tschermak in Vienna and Daubrée in Paris. They assumed that the meteorites were either thrown into space by volcanic explosions or that these celestial bodies were shattered somehow. A careful study of the asteroids and their orbits (see also the orbits of the meteorites Sikhote-Alin and Příbram) suggest that the shattered parent body was one or several planets orbiting the Sun between Mars and Jupiter. In this view, "Meteorites and asteroids are nothing but witnesses of a past episode in the history of our solar system." Other scientists assume that the breakup occurred in interstellar space. That meteorites originated from the breakup of a larger parent body is suggested, among other things, by their chemical and mineral composition. In spite of their apparent diversity, both show a remarkable regularity, allowing, as we saw, the classification of meteorites into a reasonable system. We do not find arbitrary combinations of matter, but only those which we would expect, in the light of all our chemical and physical knowledge, if a celestial body somewhat similar to the earth were broken up. A further argument for this hypothesis is the fragment-like shape of meteorites. It is also supported by the observation that many of the smaller asteroids are not spherical in shape as are all other celestial bodies, but have an irregular, angular outline, suggesting that they are fragments of larger bodies.*

As a summary of this section and as a final conclusion of all the observational and factual material presented to the reader in this book, one can state: In the one and a half centuries that have passed since Chladni postulated an extra-terrestrial origin of meteorites, not a single fact has turned up to contradict this view, although a

*[Many of the larger asteroids down to a radius of 60 km. are spherical or nearly so. This may imply that they are original accretions, while the smaller ones and the meteorites are merely the collisional debris from the breakup of the larger ones. However, some scientists argue that the meteorite parent body was larger than any of the present-day asteroids; possibly as large as the Moon or even Mars.—Translator]

great deal of new observational material and new knowledge have been acquired. The origin of meteorites has not yet been finally settled, although there is scarcely any doubt that they belong to the solar system. The question of the formation of meteorites has also not yet been settled conclusively. Virtually all observations seem to favor an origin as fragments of a larger parent body rather than an origin as individual entities, but the nature of this parent body (or bodies) is still open to debate.

In order to obtain definitive answers to these questions, much intensive work will be necessary. Most of this work will have to be done by the experts, of course, who can apply the tools of modern physical science with ever-increasing force to the study of these most interesting objects. But in contrast to many other branches of natural science, meteoritics is in the enviable position of being able to invite large groups of the public with an interest in natural science to active participation, instead of a merely passive reception of research findings. We have seen of what great importance is the entire complex of phenomena associated with the fall of a meteorite. Even limited and apparently insignificant observations by laymen can, if sufficiently numerous and made with sufficient accuracy, provide the basis for far-reaching and important conclusions. The author will be most pleased if he has succeeded in arousing interest and the desire to participate actively in our science, in at least some of the readers of this little book.

APPENDIX

METEORITE COLLECTIONS

As soon as the true nature of meteorites was recognized, intensive efforts toward their collection began. Several large collections were established which are of very great importance for the study of meteorites. It is not possible to obtain material abundantly from the field as can be done with terrestrial rocks. Many meteorites are unique, and for a thorough study, large specimens are needed as well as ample material for comparison.

In the U.S.S.R., the Academy of Sciences in Moscow appointed a special committee to administer the Moscow collection. It has been very active in the recovery of meteorites from the vast area of the U.S.S.R. In the United States, too, an Institute for Meteorites was established at the University of New Mexico in Albuquerque.

Probably the oldest and still one of the most important meteorite collections is that of the former Imperial Court Museum in Vienna. Well over six hundred falls and finds are represented here. The collections of the British Museum in London and the Natural History Museum in Paris are of similar age and extent. In Germany, the collections of the Universities of Berlin, Bonn, Tübingen, and Göttingen are particularly worthy of mention, although smaller collections are found at nearly all universities. In the United States, meteorite collections have expanded considerably in recent years. The Chicago Natural History Museum contains probably the largest meteorite collection in the world. Other very large collections are found in the United States National Museum (Smithsonian Institution) in Washington, D.C.; in the American Museum of Natural History in New York; at Harvard University; and in the Nininger Meteorite Collection at the University of Arizona in Tempe. Other large collections exist in Stockholm, Calcutta, and Mexico City.

TEKTITES

By way of an appendix, we want to mention a group of objects whose origin has not yet been definitely established and which, though not meteorites themselves, seem to stand in close relationship to the meteorites. They are glassy bodies, bottle-green to blackish, called "tektites." They are found in gravels ranging in age from Upper to Lower Tertiary, Diluvial and Alluvial, in Czechoslovakia, near Budějovice and Třebice (moldavites, named after the Moldau River, or "bottlestones," because of their bottle-green color); in former Indochina, in Thailand, and on the Malayan Peninsula; on the islands of Java, Flores, Billiton (billitonites), Borneo, and the Philippines (rizalites); also in Southern Australia and Tasmania (australites); near Ouellée, on the Ivory Coast in Africa, and in Texas and Georgia in the United States (bediasites). Glasses of somewhat different nature have been found in the Libyan Desert. Other glasses from Paucartambo and Macusani in Peru are apparently not related to tektites. Tektites are usually quite small, rarely exceeding the size of a man's fist. They often have characteristic surface features and range in shape from irregular to spherical, ellipsoidal, barrel, pear, dumbbell, or button shape. Figures 99–109 illustrate this variety of shapes. Chemically, they are completely distinct from the meteorites. They are rich in silica (70–97 per cent SiO_2) and resemble in their composition clayey sandstones or almost pure quartz sands. Analysis of their trace element content at the University of Jena shows that the composition of tektites is not at all dissimilar to that of terrestrial rocks. The concentration of the less volatile elements in tektites is the same as that of the above-mentioned rocks, whereas the lower boiling elements, such as copper, germanium, tin, and lead, depart from the terrestrial values to varying degree, but always in the same direction: their concentration in tektites is always lower than in terrestrial sedimentary rocks. One could assume that these readily volatile elements have in part vaporized during the melting of these glasses. Mineralogically, they consist almost entirely of glass. Only in Libyan Desert glass were crystals of quartz and cristobalite observed.

The mystery of the origin of these glasses has, of course, stimulated many hypotheses. Nearly all of these could be rejected as inadequate or highly improbable. Even the hypothesis which was

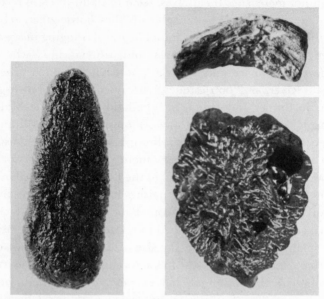

FIGS. 99–101.—Moldavites from Czechoslovakia: Fig. 99 (left), about two-thirds natural size; Fig. 100 (above, right), natural size; Fig. 101 (below, right), natural size.

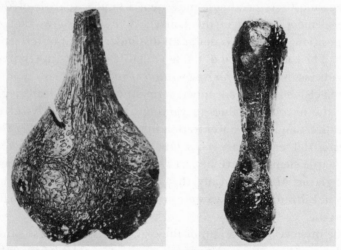

FIGS. 102–3.—Tektites from former Indochina. (After Lacroix, in *Arch. Mus. Nation. Hist. Natur.*, Paris, 1932.)

FIGS. 104–6.—Billitonites from Billiton Island: Fig. 104, slightly reduced; Fig. 105, slightly enlarged; Fig. 106, slightly enlarged.

FIGS. 107–9.—Australites from Australia, about natural size.

finally accepted as the most probable by many meteoriticists, that the tektites are glassy meteorites, does not stand up to criticism. The fall of such a glass meteorite has not been observed. Thus, in 1936, it was a step forward when the British meteoriticist L. J. Spencer suggested the new hypothesis, that these mysterious glasses were nothing but the glassy remains of former impacts of giant meteorites (see p. 40). He was able to marshal rather convincing evidence for such an origin, at least for the Queenstownites of Tasmania, a group of glasses which had been regarded as tektites up to that time. The glasses found in what appears to be a crater-field near Aouelloul in the western Sahara also seem to be of the same origin. For the remaining tektites there are still some difficulties, originating primarily in the apparent independence of their composition from that of the underlying rock. This would seem to require that the individual tektite groups were formed by the impact of "super-giant meteorites" which melted whole portions of the earth's crust in this process. Spencer's hypothesis has the advantage that it may eventually be tested conclusively as our knowledge in this area increases.

ELEMENT CONCENTRATIONS IN ORDINARY CHONDRITES
(ATOMS/10^6 Si ATOMS)

| ATOMIC NO. | ELEMENT | | CONCENTRATION |
	Symbol	Name	
1	H	Hydrogen	47,000
2	He	Helium	0.11
3	Li	Lithium	50
4	Be	Beryllium	0.64
5	B	Boron	40
6	C	Carbon	2,000
7	N	Nitrogen	90
8	O	Oxygen	3,440,000
9	F	Fluorine	300
10	Ne	Neon	0.0015
11	Na	Sodium	46,000
12	Mg	Magnesium	930,000
13	Al	Aluminum	84,000
14	Si	Silicon	1,000,000
15	P	Phosphorus	4,400
16	S	Sulfur	105,000
17	Cl	Chlorine	1,000
18	Ar	Argon	0.4
19	K	Potassium	3,300
20	Ca	Calcium	53,000
21	Sc	Scandium	30
22	Ti	Titanium	2,200
23	V	Vanadium	160
24	Cr	Chromium	7,700
25	Mn	Manganese	5,800
26	Fe	Iron	690,000
27	Co	Cobalt	1,200
28	Ni	Nickel	36,000
29	Cu	Copper	190
30	Zn	Zinc	120
31	Ga	Gallium	12
32	Ge	Germanium	19
33	As	Arsenic	4.7
34	Se	Selenium	17
35	Br	Bromine	2
36	Kr	Krypton	?
37	Rb	Rubidium	7
38	Sr	Strontium	20
39	Y	Yttrium	3.6
40	Zr	Zirconium	65
41	Nb	Niobium	1
42	Mo	Molybdenum	2.5
43	Tc	Technetium	

ELEMENT CONCENTRATIONS IN ORDINARY CHONDRITES
(ATOMS/10^6 Si ATOMS)

	Element		
Atomic No.	Symbol	Name	Concentration
44	Ru	Ruthenium	1.6
45	Rh	Rhodium	0.27
46	Pd	Palladium	1.1
47	Ag	Silver	0.13
48	Cd	Cadmium	0.064
49	In	Indium	0.0013
50	Sn	Tin	1.1
51	Sb	Antimony	0.1
52	Te	Tellurium	1
53	I	Iodine	0.05
54	Xe	Xenon	0.000007
55	Cs	Cesium	0.12
56	Ba	Barium	4.0
57	La	Lanthanum	0.4
58	Ce	Cerium	1.1
59	Pr	Praseodymium	0.2
60	Nd	Neodymium	0.8
61	Pm	Promethium	
62	Sm	Samarium	0.3
63	Eu	Europium	0.1
64	Gd	Gadolinium	0.4
65	Tb	Terbium	0.06
66	Dy	Dysprosium	0.3
67	Ho	Holmium	0.08
68	Er	Erbium	0.2
69	Tm	Thulium	0.04
70	Yb	Ytterbium	0.2
71	Lu	Lutecium	0.03
72	Hf	Hafnium	1.2
73	Ta	Tantalūm	0.02
74	W	Wolfram (Tungsten)	0.12
75	Re	Rhenium	0.0028
76	Os	Osmium	0.6
77	Ir	Iridium	0.37
78	Pt	Platinum	1.3
79	Au	Gold	0.13
80	Hg	Mercury	0.076
81	Tl	Thallium	0.0007
82	Pb	Lead	0.15
83	Bi	Bismuth	0.002
90	Th	Thorium	0.026
92	U	Uranium	0.0075

TABLE OF METEORITE MINERALS

	Mineral*	Chemical Composition
Elements	Diamond	Carbon C
	Graphite	Carbon C
	Nickel-iron	Alloy of iron (Fe) and nickel (Ni)
	Kamacite	ca. 6% Ni
	Taenite	ca. 13–48% Ni
Sulfides, Phosphides, Carbides	*Oldhamite	Calcium sulfide CaS
	*	Magnesium sulfide, MgS
	Pyrrhotite	} Iron sulfide FeS
	Troilite	
	Pentlandite	Nickel sulfide NiS
	*Daubréelite	Iron chromium sulfide $FeCr_2S_4$
	*Schreibersite	} Iron phosphide $(Fe,Ni,Co)_3P$
	*Rhabdite	
	Cohenite	Iron carbide $(Fe,Ni,Co)_3C$
	*Moissanite	Silicon carbide SiC
Chlorides	*Lawrencite	Iron (II) chloride $FeCl_2$
Oxides	Quartz	Silicon dioxide, SiO_2
	Tridymite	Silicon dioxide, SiO_2
	Magnetite	Iron (II, III) oxide Fe_3O_4
	Chromite	Iron-chromium oxide $FeCr_2O_4$
	Ilmenite	Iron titanate $FeTiO_3$
Silicates	Plagioclase	Solid solution of albite (sodium aluminum silicate $NaAlSi_3O_8$) and anorthite (calcium aluminum silicate $CaAlSi_2O_8$)
	*Maskelynite	Glass of plagioclase composition
	Enstatite, bronzite, hypersthene	Solid solution of magnesium and iron metasilicates $MgSiO_3$–$FeSiO_3$
	Clinoenstatite-Clinohypersthene..	Solid solution of magnesium and iron metasilicates $MgSiO_3$–$FeSiO_3$
	Diopside	Magnesium calcium silicate $MgCa(SiO_3)_2$
	Augite	Magnesium iron calcium silicate containing aluminum and trivalent iron
	Forsterite	Magnesium silicate Mg_2SiO_4
	Olivine	Magnesium iron silicate $(Mg,Fe)_2SiO_4$
	Chlorite-serpentine-like mineral	Hydrous magnesium iron silicate
Phosphates	Apatite	Calcium phosphate containing chlorine
	*Merillite	Sodium calcium phosphate
	*Farringtonite	Magnesium phosphate $[Mg_3 (PO_4)_2]$

* = Minerals that do not occur on Earth

SUBJECT INDEX

CRATER INDEX